Reading STREET

Grade 5

Scott Foresman
Weekly Tests
Teacher's Manual

PEARSON

Glenview, Illinois • Boston, Massachusetts • Chandler, Arizona • Upper Saddle River, New Jersey

The Pearson Promise

As the largest educational publishing company in the world, Pearson is committed to providing you with curriculum that not only meets the Common Core State Standards, but also supports your implementation of these standards with your students.

Pearson has aligned the Common Core State Standards to every grade level of *Scott Foresman Reading Street*, our premier educational curriculum. This product provides an alignment of the Common Core State Standards to the Grade 5 assessment items in *Scott Foresman Reading Street Weekly Tests*.

We value your partnership highly and look forward to continuing our mission to provide educational materials that fully satisfy your classroom needs.

ISBN-13: 978-0-328-68134-1
ISBN-10:   0-328-68134-2
5 6 7 8 9 10 V001 15 14 13 12

CONTENTS

Unit 1 Meeting Challenges

Unit 2 Doing the Right Thing

Unit 3 Inventors and Artists

Unit 4 Adapting

Unit 5 Adventurers

Unit 6 The Unexpected

OVERVIEW

The Weekly Tests are an important part of the wide array of formal tests and classroom assessments that support instruction in Scott Foresman *Reading Street*. These tests are designed to measure student progress based on the vocabulary, word analysis, and comprehension skills taught each week. Progress on the Weekly Tests is critical for determining whether the student is mastering the weekly target skills.

This Teacher's Manual includes the following: (1) a description of the Weekly Tests, (2) instructions for administering the tests, (3) instructions for scoring and recording test results, (4) reproducible charts on which to track the progress of your students, (5) the answers to the tests, and (6) alignments to the Common Core State Standards (in the Item Analysis charts and at the bottom of each student test page).

DESCRIPTION OF THE WEEKLY TESTS

In Grade 5, there are 30 tests—one for each week in the Scott Foresman *Reading Street* program.

Each test contains 4 subtests:

- The **Vocabulary** subtest consists of 5–7 multiple-choice questions that assess student knowledge of the week's selection vocabulary words.

- The **Word Analysis** subtest consists of 5–7 multiple-choice questions that assess student understanding of the week's word analysis skill.

- The **Comprehension** subtest consists of a reading passage and 8 multiple-choice questions. At least 5 of the questions assess the week's target comprehension skill. At least 1 question assesses the week's review comprehension skill. Some tests also contain 1 or 2 questions that assess other reading comprehension skills.

- The **Writing** subtest consists of a writing prompt that asks students to respond to the main selection in the Student Edition.

ADMINISTERING THE WEEKLY TESTS

The Weekly Tests should be administered at the end of Day 5 in each week.

These tests are not intended to be timed. However, for the purposes of scheduling, planning, and practicing for timed-test situations, the tests can be administered in 45 minutes—approximately 15 minutes for the Vocabulary and Word Analysis subtests, 15 minutes for the Comprehension subtest, and 15 minutes for the Writing subtest.

SCORING THE WEEKLY TESTS

Answer keys for the Weekly Tests begin on page 1. Refer to the answer key for the test you are scoring and mark each multiple-choice question as either correct (1 point) or incorrect (0 points). To score the Writing subtest, refer to the rubrics that begin on page T19.

When you have finished scoring a student's test, complete the appropriate row on the Student Progress Chart and the Class Progress Chart. Doing so allows you to keep track of your students' total scores as well as their scores on each of the individual subtests. The chart can also help you monitor your students' progress throughout the year.

The target comprehension skill of the week is the skill whose standard has at least 5 questions dedicated to it on the Reading Comprehension subtest. To assess whether a student has mastered the skill on a particular test, look at the number of items the student had correct. If the student missed more than 1 question on the target comprehension skill of the week, then the student needs reteaching and more practice. Refer to the Item Analysis chart that begins on page T9 to identify the skills assessed on each test and the Common Core State Standard aligned to each skill.

RETEACHING OPTIONS

If a student performs poorly on a Weekly Test or shows a lack of adequate progress during the year, use the Review Lessons in the Scott Foresman *Reading Street* Teacher's Editions and provide the student with additional opportunities to practice the selection vocabulary and target skills.

Scott Foresman *Reading Street*
Student Weekly Test Progress Chart—Grade 5

Student Name: _____

Test	Vocabulary	Word Analysis OPTIONAL	Comprehension	Multiple-Choice Total	Writing	TOTAL
Weekly Test 1	/7	/5	/8	/20		
Weekly Test 2	/7	/5	/8	/20		
Weekly Test 3	/7	/5	/8	/20		
Weekly Test 4	/7	/5	/8	/20		
Weekly Test 5	/6	/6	/8	/20		
Weekly Test 6	/7	/5	/8	/20		
Weekly Test 7	/7	/5	/8	/20		
Weekly Test 8	/7	/5	/8	/20		
Weekly Test 9	/7	/5	/8	/20		
Weekly Test 10	/7	/5	/8	/20		
Weekly Test 11	/5	/7	/8	/20		
Weekly Test 12	/7	/5	/8	/20		
Weekly Test 13	/7	/5	/8	/20		
Weekly Test 14	/7	/5	/8	/20		
Weekly Test 15	/6	/6	/8	/20		
Weekly Test 16	/7	/5	/8	/20		
Weekly Test 17	/5	/7	/8	/20		
Weekly Test 18	/6	/6	/8	/20		
Weekly Test 19	/6	/6	/8	/20		
Weekly Test 20	/7	/5	/8	/20		
Weekly Test 21	/7	/5	/8	/20		
Weekly Test 22	/7	/5	/8	/20		
Weekly Test 23	/6	/6	/8	/20		
Weekly Test 24	/6	/6	/8	/20		
Weekly Test 25	/5	/7	/8	/20		
Weekly Test 26	/7	/5	/8	/20		
Weekly Test 27	/7	/5	/8	/20		
Weekly Test 28	/6	/6	/8	/20		
Weekly Test 29	/6	/6	/8	/20		
Weekly Test 30	/7	/5	/8	/20		

Scott Foresman *Reading Street*
Class Weekly Test Progress Chart—Grade 5

Teacher's Name: _____

Student Name	1	2	3	4	5	6	7	8	9	10	11	12	13	14	15	16	17	18	19	20	21	22	23	24	25	26	27	28	29	30
																Weekly Test Total Score														
1																														
2																														
3																														
4																														
5																														
6																														
7																														
8																														
9																														
10																														
11																														
12																														
13																														
14																														
15																														
16																														
17																														
18																														
19																														
20																														
21																														
22																														
23																														
24																														
25																														
26																														
27																														
28																														
29																														
30																														

Weekly Test Item Analysis—Grade 5

TEST	SECTION	ITEMS	SKILL	COMMON CORE STATE STANDARD
Weekly Test 1	**Vocabulary**	1–7	Understand and use new vocabulary	Language 5.c.
	Word Analysis	8–12	Suffix -*ly*	Language 4.
	Comprehension	13–17, 20	◎ Literary Elements: Character and plot	13–15, 17, 20: Literature 1. 16: Literature 3.
		19	Draw conclusions	Literature 1.
		18	**R** Sequence	Literature 1.
	Written Response	Look Back and Write	Respond to literature	Writing 4. (Also Language 1, 2.)
Weekly Test 2	**Vocabulary**	1–7	Understand and use new vocabulary	Language 5.c.
	Word Analysis	8–12	Greek and Latin roots	Language 4.b.
	Comprehension	14, 16–19	◎ Cause and effect	Literature 1.
		13, 15	Sequence	Literature 1.
		20	**R** Literary Elements: Character, setting, plot	Literature 1.
	Written Response	Look Back and Write	Respond to literature	Writing 2. (Also Writing 9.)
Weekly Test 3	**Vocabulary**	1–7	Understand and use new vocabulary	Language 5.c.
	Word Analysis	8–12	Compound words	Foundational Skills 3.a.
	Comprehension	13, 14, 17, 19, 20	◎ Literary Elements: Theme and setting	13, 14, 19: Literature 1. 17, 20: Literature 2.
		15, 16, 18	**R** Literary Elements: Character and plot	Literature 1.
	Written Response	Look Back and Write	Respond to literature	Writing 2. (Also Writing 2.a., 2.b., 4., Language 1.)

Weekly Test Item Analysis—Grade 5

TEST	SECTION	ITEMS	SKILL	COMMON CORE STATE STANDARD
Weekly Test 4	**Vocabulary**	1–7	Understand and use new vocabulary	Language 5.c.
	Word Analysis	8–12	Shades of meaning	Language 5.c.
	Comprehension	13–15, 17, 19	◎ Fact and opinion	Informational Text 1.
		18, 20	Draw conclusions	Informational Text 1.
		16	**R** Cause and effect	Informational Text 1.
	Written Response	Look Back and Write	Respond to literature	Writing 2.b. (Also Writing 2.c., Language 1., 3.a.)
Weekly Test 5	**Vocabulary**	1–6	Understand and use new vocabulary	Language 5.c.
	Word Analysis	7–12	Suffix *-ing*	Language 4.a.
	Comprehension	14–16, 18, 19	◎ Cause and effect	Informational Text 3.
		13, 20	Draw conclusions, Main idea and details	13: Informational Text 3. 20: Informational Text 2.
		17	**R** Graphic sources	Informational Text 7.
	Written Response	Look Back and Write	Respond to literature	Writing 2.b. (Also Informational Text 1., Writing 2.a., 4.)
Weekly Test 6	**Vocabulary**	1–7	Understand and use new vocabulary	Language 5.c.
	Word Analysis	8–12	Spanish word origin	Language 5.c.
	Comprehension	13, 14, 15, 17, 18	◎ Compare and contrast	13, 17, 18: Literature 1. 14, 15: Literature 3.
		16, 19	Draw conclusions	Literature 1.
		20	**R** Author's purpose	Literature 2.
	Written Response	Look Back and Write	Respond to literature	Writing 3.b. (Also Literature 1., Writing 3., Language 1., 3.)

Weekly Test Item Analysis—Grade 5

TEST	SECTION	ITEMS	SKILL	COMMON CORE STATE STANDARD
Weekly Test 7	**Vocabulary**	1–7	Understand and use new vocabulary	Language 5.c.
	Word Analysis	8–12	French word origins	Language 5.c.
	Comprehension	13, 14, 17, 18, 20	◉ Sequence	13: Informational Text 3. 14, 17, 18, 20: Informational Text 1.
		15, 16	Draw conclusions	Informational Text 1.
		19	**R** Compare and contrast	Informational Text 3.
	Written Response	Look Back and Write	Respond to literature	Writing 3.b. (Also Language 1., 3.)
Weekly Test 8	**Vocabulary**	1–7	Understand and use new vocabulary	Language 5.c.
	Word Analysis	8–12	Suffixes -tion, -ion	Language 5.c.
	Comprehension	14, 15, 17–19	◉ Compare and contrast	14, 17: Literature 3. 15, 18, 19: Literature 1.
		13, 20	Draw conclusions	Literature 1.
		16	**R** Sequence	Literature 1.
	Written Response	Look Back and Write	Respond to literature	Writing 2.b. (Also Literature 1., Writing 2., 4., 9., Language 1.)
Weekly Test 9	**Vocabulary**	1–7	Understand and use new vocabulary	Language 5.c.
	Word Analysis	8–12	Spanish word origins	Language 5.c.
	Comprehension	13, 14, 18–20	◉ Author's purpose	Informational Text 8.
		15	Cause and effect	Informational Text 1.
		17	Fact and opinion	Informational Text 1.
		16	**R** Compare and contrast	Informational Text 3.
	Written Response	Look Back and Write	Respond to literature	Writing 3.b. (Also Literature 2., Writing 3., 4., 5.)

Weekly Test Item Analysis—Grade 5

TEST	SECTION	ITEMS	SKILL	COMMON CORE STATE STANDARD
Weekly Test 10	**Vocabulary**	1–7	Understand and use new vocabulary	Language 5.c.
	Word Analysis	8–12	Word families	Foundational Skills 3.a.
	Comprehension	13, 15, 17, 19, 20	◉ Author's purpose	Informational Text 8.
		16	Cause and effect	Informational Text 3.
		18	Generalize	Informational Text 1.
		14	**R** Literary Elements: Theme and setting	Informational Text 2.
	Written Response	Look Back and Write	Respond to literature	Writing 3.b. (Also Literature 1., Writing 3.a., 3.d., Language 1., 3.)
Weekly Test 11	**Vocabulary**	1–5	Understand and use new vocabulary	Language 5.c.
	Word Analysis	6–12	Shades of meaning	Language 5.c.
	Comprehension	13–16, 19	◉ Sequence	Informational Text 1.
		17, 20	Fact and opinion, Draw conclusions	Informational Text 3.
		18	**R** Cause and effect	Informational Text 2.
	Written Response	Look Back and Write	Respond to literature	Writing 1. (Also Writing 3.a., 3.b., 3.c., Language 1.)
Weekly Test 12	**Vocabulary**	1–7	Understand and use new vocabulary	Language 5.c.
	Word Analysis	8–12	Greek and Latin roots	Language 4.b.
	Comprehension	13, 15, 18–20	◉ Main idea and details	Informational Text 2.
		14, 17	Draw conclusions	Informational Text 1.
		16	**R** Fact and opinion	Informational Text 1.
	Written Response	Look Back and Write	Respond to literature	Writing 1.a. (Also Writing 5., Language 1.)

Weekly Test Item Analysis—Grade 5

TEST	SECTION	ITEMS	SKILL	COMMON CORE STATE STANDARD
Weekly Test 13	**Vocabulary**	1–7	Understand and use new vocabulary	Language 5.c.
	Word Analysis	8–12	Suffixes *-tion, -sion*	Language 2.e.
	Comprehension	13, 14, 16, 18, 19	◉ Fact and opinion	Informational Text 1.
		15, 17	Graphic sources, Draw conclusions	Informational Text 1.
		20	R Main idea and details	Informational Text 2.
	Written Response	Look Back and Write	Respond to literature	Writing 2. (Also Writing 4., 5.)
Weekly Test 14	**Vocabulary**	1–7	Understand and use new vocabulary	Language 5.c.
	Word Analysis	8–12	Suffix *-ous*	Language 5.c.
	Comprehension	14, 16–18, 20	◉ Main idea and details	Informational Text 2.
		13	Draw conclusions	Informational Text 1.
		19	Generalize	Informational Text 1.
		15	R Fact and opinion	Informational Text 1.
	Written Response	Look Back and Write	Respond to literature	Writing 2.b. (Also Writing 2.d., Language 1.)
Weekly Test 15	**Vocabulary**	1–6	Understand and use new vocabulary	Language 5.c.
	Word Analysis	7–12	Compound words	Foundational Skills 3.a.
	Comprehension	14, 15, 16, 18, 19	◉ Graphic sources	Informational Text 7.
		13	Draw conclusions	Informational Text 1.
		17	Main idea and details	Informational Text 2.
		20	R Author's purpose	Informational Text 8.
	Written Response	Look Back and Write	Respond to literature	Writing 2. (Also Writing 4., Language 1.)

Weekly Test Item Analysis—Grade 5

TEST	SECTION	ITEMS	SKILL	COMMON CORE STATE STANDARD
Weekly Test 16	**Vocabulary**	1–7	Understand and use new vocabulary	Language 5.c.
	Word Analysis	8–12	Word endings *-ing, -ed, -s*	Language 1.
	Comprehension	13, 14, 15, 18, 19	◉ Draw conclusions	13–14, 18: Literature 1. 15: Literature 4. 19: Literature 2.
		16, 17	Author's purpose	Literature 1.
		20	**R** Literary Elements: Theme and setting	Literature 2.
	Written Response	Look Back and Write	Respond to literature	Writing 9. (Also Literature 1., Writing 4., 5., 9.a., 10. Language 1., 2.)
Weekly Test 17	**Vocabulary**	1–5	Understand and use new vocabulary	Language 5.c.
	Word Analysis	6–12	Suffixes *-ly, -ian*	Language 5.c.
	Comprehension	13, 14, 17–19	◉ Generalize	Literature 1.
		15, 16, 20	**R** Draw conclusions	Literature 1.
	Written Response	Look Back and Write	Respond to literature	Writing 9. (Also Literature 1., Writing 4., 5., Language 1., 2.)
Weekly Test 18	**Vocabulary**	1–6	Understand and use new vocabulary	Language 5.c.
	Word Analysis	7–12	Suffix *-ize*	Language 5.c.
	Comprehension	13–16, 18	◉ Graphic sources	Informational Text 7.
		19, 20	Main idea and details	Informational Text 2.
		17	**R** Author's purpose	Informational Text 1.
	Written Response	Look Back and Write	Respond to literature	Writing 2. (Also Informational Text 1., Writing 4., 5., Language 1., 2.)

Weekly Test Item Analysis—Grade 5

TEST	SECTION	ITEMS	SKILL	COMMON CORE STATE STANDARD
Weekly Test 19	**Vocabulary**	1–6	Understand and use new vocabulary	Language 5.c.
	Word Analysis	7–12	Prefixes *com-, pro-, epi-*	Language 4.b.
	Comprehension	13, 14, 16, 18, 19	◎ Generalize	Informational Text 1.
		17, 20	Main idea and details	Informational Text 2.
		15	R Draw conclusions	Informational Text 1.
	Written Response	Look Back and Write	Respond to literature	Writing 9.a. (Also Literature 1., 2., Writing 4., 5., 10., Language 1., 2.)
Weekly Test 20	**Vocabulary**	1–7	Understand and use new vocabulary	Language 5.c.
	Word Analysis	8–12	Idioms	Language 5.b.
	Comprehension	13–17	◎ Draw conclusions	Informational Text 1.
		18, 19	Sequence	Informational Text 1.
		20	R Generalize	Informational Text 1.
	Written Response	Look Back and Write	Respond to literature	Writing 9.a. (Also Literature 1., Writing 4., 5., 9.a., 10., Language 1., 2.)
Weekly Test 21	**Vocabulary**	1–7	Understand and use new vocabulary	Language 5.c.
	Word Analysis	8–12	Prefixes *im-, ate-*	Language 4.b.
	Comprehension	13–17	◎ Literary Elements: Character and plot	13, 17: Literature 3. 14–16: Literature 1.
		19, 20	Draw conclusions	Literature 1.
		18	R Author's purpose	Literature 1.
	Written Response	Look Back and Write	Respond to literature	Writing 1. (Also Writing 5., Language 1.)

Weekly Test Item Analysis—Grade 5

TEST	SECTION	ITEMS	SKILL	COMMON CORE STATE STANDARD
Weekly Test 22	**Vocabulary**	1–7	Understand and use new vocabulary	Language 5.c.
	Word Analysis	8–12	Acronyms	Language 4.
	Comprehension	13–16, 18	◉ Graphic sources	Informational Text 7.
		17, 19	Draw conclusions	Informational Text 3.
		20	**R** Main idea and details	Informational Text 2.
	Written Response	Look Back and Write	Respond to literature	Writing 9. (Also Writing 2.a., 4., Language 1.)
Weekly Test 23	**Vocabulary**	1–6	Understand and use new vocabulary	Language 5.c.
	Word Analysis	7–12	Greek and Latin roots	Language 4.b.
	Comprehension	14, 16, 17, 19, 20	◉ Author's purpose	Informational Text 8.
		13, 18	Main idea and details	Informational Text 2.
		15	**R** Graphic sources	Informational Text 7.
	Written Response	Look Back and Write	Respond to literature	Writing 4. (Also Writing 2., 2.b., 2.c., Language 1.)
Weekly Test 24	**Vocabulary**	1–6	Understand and use new vocabulary	Language 5.c.
	Word Analysis	7–12	Complex spelling patterns -ous, -ious, -eous	Language 2.e.
	Comprehension	14–16, 18, 20	◉ Cause and effect	Informational Text 3.
		17	Draw conclusions	Informational Text 1.
		19	Main idea and details	Informational Text 2.
		13	**R** Author's purpose	Informational Text 8.
	Written Response	Look Back and Write	Respond to literature	Writing 1.b. (Also Writing 1.d., Language 1.)

Weekly Test Item Analysis—Grade 5

TEST	SECTION	ITEMS	SKILL	COMMON CORE STATE STANDARD
Weekly Test 25	**Vocabulary**	1–5	Understand and use new vocabulary	Language 5.c.
	Word Analysis	6–12	Morphemes	Language 5.c.
	Comprehension	15–17, 19, 20	◉ Generalize	Informational Text 1.
		14, 18	Main idea and details	Informational Text 2.
		13	R Graphic sources	Informational Text 7.
	Written Response	Look Back and Write	Respond to literature	Writing 2.b. (Also Writing 4., Language 1.)
Weekly Test 26	**Vocabulary**	1–6	Understand and use new vocabulary	Language 5.c.
	Word Analysis	7–12	Compound words	Language 3.a.
	Comprehension	13–15, 17–19	◉ Draw conclusions	Informational Text 3.
		20	Compare and contrast	Informational Text 3.
		16	R Generalize	Informational Text 1.
	Written Response	Look Back and Write	Respond to literature	Literature 4. (Also Writing 1.a., 1.b., 1.c., Language 1., 3.)
Weekly Test 27	**Vocabulary**	1–7	Understand and use new vocabulary	Language 5.c.
	Word Analysis	8–12	Russian word origin	Language 5.c.
	Comprehension	15–18, 20	◉ Main idea and details	Informational Text 2.
		13	Author's purpose	Informational Text 1.
		14	Draw conclusions	Informational Text 1.
		19	R Sequence	Informational Text 1.
	Written Response	Look Back and Write	Respond to literature	Writing 2. (Also Language 1., 3.)

Weekly Test Item Analysis—Grade 5

TEST	SECTION	ITEMS	SKILL	COMMON CORE STATE STANDARD
Weekly Test 28	**Vocabulary**	1–6	Understand and use new vocabulary	Language 5.c.
	Word Analysis	7–12	Complex spelling patterns ci=/sh/, ti=/sh/, ous=/us/	Language 2.e.
	Comprehension	13–15, 18, 19	◉ Compare and contrast	Literature 3.
		16	Main idea and details	Literature 2.
		17, 20	**R** Draw conclusions	Literature 1.
	Written Response	Look Back and Write	Respond to literature	Writing 5.b. (Also Literature 4., Writing 1.a., 1.b., 1.c., Language 1., 3., 5.b.)
Weekly Test 29	**Vocabulary**	1–6	Understand and use new vocabulary	Language 5.c.
	Word Analysis	7–12	Word families	Language 5.c.
	Comprehension	14–16, 18, 20	◉ Fact and opinion	Informational Text 1.
		17	Draw conclusions	Informational Text 1.
		13, 19	**R** Main idea and details	Informational Text 2.
	Written Response	Look Back and Write	Respond to literature	Writing 1. (Also Writing 1.a., 1.c., 4., Language 1., 3.)
Weekly Test 30	**Vocabulary**	1–7	Understand and use new vocabulary	Language 5.c.
	Word Analysis	8–12	Compound words	Foundational Skills 3.a.
	Comprehension	13, 14, 18–20	◉ Sequence	Literature 1.
		15–17	**R** Draw conclusions	Literature 1.
	Written Response	Look Back and Write	Respond to literature	Writing 1. (Also Literature 1., Language 1., 3.)

Comprehension Target Skill Coverage

How can the Weekly Tests predict student success on Unit Benchmark Tests?

Each Unit Benchmark Test, as well as assessing overall student reading ability, concentrates on two skills taught and/or reviewed during the unit by including several questions on those skills. In order to ensure that comprehension target skill can be accurately learned and then tested, students learn each target skill through a combination of being taught and reviewing the skill multiple times before testing occurs. The charts on the pages that follow show the units/weeks where the target comprehension skills are taught and where they are tested on Weekly Tests. Based on the student's number of correct answers for each tested target skill, the teacher will know whether a student has gained the necessary skill knowledge before the Unit Test is given. A low score on the Weekly Tests probably indicates a need for closer review of the student's performance and perhaps additional instruction. It is important to understand that these tests provide only one look at the student's progress and should be interpreted in conjunction with other assessments and the teacher's observation.

Using the Comprehension Target Skill Coverage Chart

To score target skill knowledge, use the Comprehension Target Skill Coverage Chart.

1. Make a copy of the appropriate Comprehension Target Skill Coverage chart for each student.

2. To score, circle the number of correct answers the student had for that skill on the appropriate Weekly Test.

3. Using the total number of correct answers for a skill, check the appropriate box under *Student Trend* to indicate whether or not the student has acquired the target skill knowledge. We recommend 90% correct as the criterion for skill aquisition at this level. Add any notes or observations that may be helpful to you and the student in later instruction.

Grade 5 — Comprehension Target Skill Coverage Chart

Student Name _____

Unit 1 Tested Skills	Weekly Test Locations	Number Correct	Student Trend
Literary Elements: Character/Plot/ Theme/Setting **Common Core State Standards** Literature 1., Literature 2., Literature 3.	Weekly Test 1	0 1 2 3 4 5 6	_____ Skill knowledge acquired _____ Skill needs further review
	Weekly Test 2	0 1	
	Weekly Test 3	0 1 2 3 4 5 6 7 8	
Cause and Effect **Common Core State Standards** Literature 1.; Informational Text 1., Informational Text 3.	Weekly Test 2	0 1 2 3 4 5	_____ Skill knowledge acquired _____ Skill needs further review
	Weekly Test 4	0 1	
	Weekly Test 5	0 1 2 3 4 5	

Unit 2 Tested Skills	Weekly Test Locations	Number Correct	Student Trend
Compare and Contrast **Common Core State Standards** Literature 1., Literature 3.; Informational Text 3.	Weekly Test 6	0 1 2 3 4 5	_____ Skill knowledge acquired _____ Skill needs further review
	Weekly Test 7	0 1	
	Weekly Test 8	0 1 2 3 4 5	
	Weekly Test 9	0 1	
Sequence **Common Core State Standards** Literature 1.; Informational Text 1., Informational Text 3.	Weekly Test 1	0 1	_____ Skill knowledge acquired _____ Skill needs further review
	Weekly Test 2	0 1 2	
	Weekly Test 7	0 1 2 3 4 5	
	Weekly Test 8	0 1	

Grade 5 — Comprehension Target Skill Coverage Chart

Student Name _____

Unit 3 Tested Skills	Weekly Test Locations	Number Correct	Student Trend
Main Idea and Supporting Details **Common Core State Standards** Informational Text 2.	Weekly Test 5	0 1	____ Skill knowledge acquired ____ Skill needs further review
	Weekly Test 12	0 1 2 3 4 5	
	Weekly Test 13	0 1	
	Weekly Test 14	0 1 2 3 4 5	
	Weekly Test 15	0 1	
Fact and Opinion **Common Core State Standards** Informational Text 1., Informational Text 3.	Weekly Test 4	0 1 2 3 4 5	____ Skill knowledge acquired ____ Skill needs further review
	Weekly Test 9	0 1	
	Weekly Test 11	0 1	
	Weekly Test 12	0 1	
	Weekly Test 13	0 1 2 3 4 5	
	Weekly Test 14	0 1	

Grade 5 — Comprehension Target Skill Coverage Chart

Student Name _____

Unit 4 Tested Skills	Weekly Test Locations	Number Correct	Student Trend
Generalize **Common Core State Standards** Literature 1.; Informational Text 1.	Weekly Test 10	0 1	
	Weekly Test 14	0 1	
	Weekly Test 17	0 1 2 3 4 5	____ Skill knowledge acquired
	Weekly Test 19	0 1 2 3 4 5	____ Skill needs further review
	Weekly Test 20	0 1	
Draw Conclusions **Common Core State Standards** Literature 1., Literature 2.; Informational Text 1., Informational Text 3.	Weekly Test 1	0 1	
	Weekly Test 4	0 1 2	
	Weekly Test 5	0 1	
	Weekly Test 6	0 1 2	
	Weekly Test 7	0 1 2	
	Weekly Test 8	0 1 2	
	Weekly Test 11	0 1	
	Weekly Test 12	0 1 2	
	Weekly Test 13	0 1	
	Weekly Test 14	0 1	
	Weekly Test 15	0 1	
	Weekly Test 16	0 1 2 3 4 5	
	Weekly Test 17	0 1 2 3	____ Skill knowledge acquired
	Weekly Test 19	0 1	____ Skill needs further review
	Weekly Test 20	0 1 2 3 4 5	

T18D

Grade 5 — Comprehension Target Skill Coverage Chart

Student Name _____

Unit 5 Tested Skills	Weekly Test Locations	Number Correct	Student Trend
Graphic Sources **Common Core State Standards** Informational Text 1, Informational Text 7.	Weekly Test 5	0 1	
	Weekly Test 13	0 1	
	Weekly Test 15	0 1 2 3 4 5	
	Weekly Test 18	0 1 2 3 4 5	
	Weekly Test 22	0 1 2 3 4 5	_____ Skill knowledge acquired
	Weekly Test 23	0 1	_____ Skill needs further review
	Weekly Test 25	0 1	
Author's Purpose **Common Core State Standards** Literature 1., Literature 2.; Informational Text 8.	Weekly Test 6	0 1	
	Weekly Test 9	0 1 2 3 4 5	
	Weekly Test 10	0 1 2 3 4 5	
	Weekly Test 15	0 1	
	Weekly Test 16	0 1 2	
	Weekly Test 18	0 1	
	Weekly Test 21	0 1	_____ Skill knowledge acquired
	Weekly Test 23	0 1 2 3 4 5	_____ Skill needs further review
	Weekly Test 24	0 1	

Grade 5 — Comprehension Target Skill Coverage Chart

Student Name _____

Unit 6 Tested Skills	Weekly Test Locations	Number Correct	Student Trend
Sequence **Common Core State Standards** Literature 1.; Informational Text 1.	Weekly Test 1	0 1	
	Weekly Test 2	0 1 2	
	Weekly Test 7	0 1 2 3 4 5	
	Weekly Test 8	0 1	____ Skill knowledge acquired
	Weekly Test 11	0 1 2 3 4 5	
	Weekly Test 20	0 1 2	____ Skill needs further review
	Weekly Test 30	0 1 2 3 4 5	
Draw Conclusions **Common Core State Standards** Literature 1., Literature 2.; Informational Text 1., Informational Text 3.	Weekly Test 1	0 1	
	Weekly Test 4	0 1 2	
	Weekly Test 5	0 1	
	Weekly Test 6	0 1 2	
	Weekly Test 7	0 1 2	
	Weekly Test 8	0 1 2	
	Weekly Test 11	0 1	
	Weekly Test 12	0 1 2	
	Weekly Test 13	0 1	
	Weekly Test 14	0 1	
	Weekly Test 15	0 1	
	Weekly Test 16	0 1 2 3 4 5	
	Weekly Test 17	0 1 2 3	
	Weekly Test 19	0 1	
	Weekly Test 20	0 1 2 3 4 5	
	Weekly Test 21	0 1 2	
	Weekly Test 22	0 1 2	
	Weekly Test 24	0 1	
	Weekly Test 26	0 1 2 3 4 5 6	
	Weekly Test 27	0 1	____ Skill knowledge acquired
	Weekly Test 28	0 1 2	
	Weekly Test 29	0 1	____ Skill needs further review
	Weekly Test 30	0 1 2 3	

SCORING RUBRICS FOR WRITING

Use one of the following rubrics (2 points or 4 points depending on your needs) to evaluate student responses on the Writing subtest. Suggested top-score responses for each week's prompt follow the rubrics.

Two-Point Scoring Rubric

2 points:

The response indicates that the student has a complete understanding of the reading concept embodied in the task. The response is accurate and complete, and fulfills all the requirements of the task. Necessary support and/or examples are included, and the information given is clearly text-based.

1 point:

The response indicates that the student has a partial understanding of the reading concept embodied in the task. The response includes information that is essentially correct and text-based, but the information is too general or too simplistic. Some of the support and/or examples may be incomplete or omitted.

0 points:

The response indicates that the student does not demonstrate an understanding of the reading concept embodied in the task. The student has either failed to respond or has provided a response that is inaccurate or has insufficient information.

Four-Point Scoring Rubric

4 points:

The response indicates that the student has a thorough understanding of the reading concept embodied in the task. The response is accurate and complete, and fulfills all the requirements of the task. Necessary support and/or examples are included, and the information given is clearly text-based.

3 points:

The response indicates that the student has an understanding of the reading concept embodied in the task. The response is accurate and fulfills all the requirements of the task, but the required support and/or details are not complete or clearly text-based.

2 points:

The response indicates that the student has a partial understanding of the reading concept embodied in the task. The response includes information that is essentially correct and text-based, but the information is too general or too simplistic. Some of the support and/or examples and requirements of the task may be incomplete or omitted.

1 point:

The response indicates that the student has a very limited understanding of the reading concept embodied in the task. The response is incomplete, may exhibit many flaws, and may not address all the requirements of the task.

0 points:

The response indicates that the student does not demonstrate an understanding of the reading concept embodied in the task. The student has either failed to respond or has provided a response that is inaccurate or has insufficient information.

Top-Level Responses

Weekly Test 1:

Top-Score Response A top-score response tells exactly what Brady does to help others.

A top-score response should include:

- He goes out on his boat in the rain to help find Mrs. DiAngelo and her son Ben.
- He finds Ben along the river and manages to pull him into the boat.
- He performs CPR and drives the boat.
- He gets Ben to paramedics who can treat him.

Weekly Test 2:

Top-Score Response A top-score response uses details to tell about how Rose faced a challenge and succeeded.

Depending on which challenge is chosen, a top-score response might include:

- Rose using Cole to launch herself onto the back of a lead steer.
- Rose controlling the stampeding lead steer.
- Rose humming a tune to the steer to calm him down.

Weekly Test 3:

Top-Score Response A top-score response uses details about how Karana overcame the physical challenge of cutting the poles.

A top-score response should include:

- She had the determination to search many days for the right trees.
- She was smart to use fire to help cut the poles.
- She made a stone knife, even though she had never made one before.

Weekly Test 4:

Top-Score Response A top-score response uses details to describe *typical Satchel style*.

A top-score response should include:

- Satchel Paige often taunted other players during games.
- He used humorous taunts to show the players and fans how confident he was.
- Satchel was also a great performer, and he used his taunts to entertain the fans.

Weekly Test 5:

Top-Score Response A top-score response uses details to tell about the several ways in which the railroad crew worked effectively together to lay ten miles of track in one day.

A top-score response should include:
- The crew used teamwork to work well together.
- The crew was efficient, with everyone working hard to do his part.
- The crew dealt well with challenges, such as the slopes.

Weekly Test 6:

Top-Score Response A top-score response uses details and an understanding of character to explain Fernando's actions.

A top-score response should include:
- Fernando realized that he did something wrong.
- Fernando's cousins knew they disobeyed their parents.
- Fernando felt guilty because he deserved a punishment.

Weekly Test 7:

Top-Score Response A top-score response explains why William Carney received the Congressional Medal of Honor and why this was significant.

A top-score response should include:
- William Carney never let the flag touch the ground during battle against Fort Wagner, and this act helped show others the way.
- He was courageous and helped give tribute to those who died to defend the flag.
- He was the first African American to be awarded the Congressional Medal of Honor.

Weekly Test 8:

Top-Score Response A top-score response uses details to show that Hsiang-ling's good deeds were rewarded and that the rewards were well deserved.

A top-score response should include:
- Hsiang-ling gave her purse to a poor bride.
- Hsiang-ling gave her porridge to a hungry woman.
- Hsiang-ling was given a job and later, half of the Lus' fortune. Then her family was found.
- An explanation of how important events give rise to and foreshadow future events.

Weekly Test 9:

Top-Score Response A top-score response will include a topic sentence, stating how Grandmother's action will add to Tony's good deed.

A top-score response should include:

- Tony's good deed was to sacrifice the saddle for his grandmother's future.
- His grandmother realized how Tony was able to buy her bracelet back.
- By promising a future rug, Grandmother signals that she is going to get better.

Weekly Test 10:

Top-Score Response A top-score response uses details to tell about Paul Revere's feelings before and during the ride.

A top-score response should include:

- Paul Revere was impatient to see the signal from the church and start his ride. He paced with a *heavy stride*.
- As soon as he saw the signal, he rode as fast as he could, his *steed flying fearless*.
- Paul Revere knew what he was doing was very important and that the nation's fate was in his hands.

Weekly Test 11:

Top-Score Response A top-score response uses details to tell about Lily's and Carlos's goals for their invention other than winning the science fair.

A top-score response should include:

- Lily and Carlos want to offer free power to everybody.
- They want to get rich from producing the machines that create the power.
- Response should explain what the student's goals would be and compare and/or contrast those goals with the goals of Lily and Carlos.

Weekly Test 12:

Top-Score Response A top-score response uses details from the text to support a position as to whether or not Leonardo's greatest dream ever came true.

A top-score response should include:

- Although Leonardo did not complete the horse, it was completed by other artists after him.
- The horse would never have been made if it were not for Leonardo's work and vision.
- The question about whether an artist's dream can come true after the artist's death.

Weekly Test 13:

Top-Score Response A top-score response uses details to explain how Waterhouse presented the dinosaur models to the public.

A top-score response should include:

- Waterhouse planned an elegant dinner party to show the models to scientists.
- After the successful dinner, Waterhouse completed other dinosaur models.
- The Queen joined thousands of people to see the models at the opening at the Crystal Palace.

Weekly Test 14:

Top-Score Response A top-score response distinguishes fact from author's opinion and uses details from the text to explain how Mahalia Jackson used the blues in a new and different way.

A top-score response should include:

- Other famous people put the gospel feeling into the blues.
- Mahalia Jackson sang church music.
- She put the blues feeling into gospel.

Weekly Test 15:

Top-Score Response A top-score response uses details to tell about how special effects in film and television are created.

A top-score response should include:

- Special effects can involve building miniature landscapes.
- Special effects may include reptile modeling.
- Filming takes place after special effects are completed.

Weekly Test 16:

Top-Score Response A top-score response uses details to tell about Wesley and the results of his project.

A top-score response should include:

- Wesley was lonely and turned to his own imagination.
- He was inventive and used his knowledge to create his own civilization.
- Although at first Wesley was scorned for being different, he made many friends by using his imagination.

Weekly Test 17:

Top-Score Response A top-score response connects Jinx's original idea about square dancing to the outcome of her getting hurt while square dancing.

A top-score response should include:
- Jinx came up with the idea of square dancing and felt that it was meant to be.
- Jinx tried many ways to convince everyone that square dancing would be a great idea.
- Jinx finally gets a chance to square dance, but she ends up getting hurt, just like she always does in gym.

Weekly Test 18:

Top-Score Response A top-score response uses factual information about soldier ants.

A top-score response should include:
- They manufacture deadly chemicals in their own bodies.
- The chemicals are stored in two big sacs.
- When threatened, they release a small amount of the chemicals, and when attacked, they spew the chemicals.

Weekly Test 19:

Top-Score Response A top-score response uses details to tell about Hannah's passion for collecting something "almost as cool" as her grandfather's old silver fountain pen.

A top-score response should include:
- Hannah collects all kinds of pens, but mainly in colors black or blue.
- Hannah is looking for the perfect pen.
- Hannah lost an old silver fountain pen that her grandfather gave her. Her passion is to find something "almost as cool."

Weekly Test 20:

Top-Score Response A top-score response should discuss the change in the dog's interest in the cousin's activity and why this reflects Gary's changing interest in gymnastics.

A top-score response should include:
- The dog is originally appreciative and interested in what Gary's cousin is doing but goes to sleep as the cousin continues to practice.
- The dog is similar to Gary, because Gary is interested in gymnastics at first but becomes weary of the practice it takes to excel in gymnastics.

Weekly Test 21:

Top-Score Response A top-score response uses details from the story to support students' opinions.

A top-score response should include:
- A clearly stated opinion about the boys' future adventures.
- The boys have had other disasters before and it didn't stop them.
- Crazy Eddie doesn't seem to mind that he makes his father nervous.

Weekly Test 22:

Top-Score Response A top-score response uses details from the events to express in first-person diary format what was happening and what Willie was feeling and thinking.

A top-score response should include:
- Willie hurrying to the lifeboats with his mother and brother amid other frantic passengers.
- A crewman holding Willie back because his hat makes him seem older than he is.
- Willie's mother pleading with the crewman until he lets Willie onto the boat.

Weekly Test 23:

Top-Score Response A top-score response uses details to compare and contrast an astronaut's role during training and during a space mission.

A top-score response should include:
- Training includes preparation for anything that could go wrong during a mission.
- Problems need to be solved during training.
- Ochoa never faced a serious problem during a mission.

Weekly Test 24:

Top-Score Response A top-score response uses details to tell about the fantastic adventures of Harry and the other explorers.

A top-score response should include:
- The explorers found prehistoric creatures of a huge size.
- The plesiosaurus was a serpent-like animal with a small head, cylinder-shaped trunk, short tail and fins, all encased in a shell.
- The ichthyosaurus was a long fish-like creature with fins.

Weekly Test 25:

Top-Score Response A top-score response uses details to tell about the buildings in a thriving Western town and should include the student's attempt to draw a map of the buildings in a town's business area and label the buildings.

A top-score response should include:
- The business buildings met the needs of the townspeople.
- Among other buildings, they included general stores, a blacksmith, a bank, a telegraph office, a doctor/barber, and a newspaper.

Weekly Test 26:

Top-Score Response A top-score response uses details to tell about misinformation regarding bats and explains the two meanings of the word "bug."

A top-score response should include:
- People wrongly think bats will hurt them.
- Few bats carry rabies and vampire bats do not feed on humans.
- Bats help people by pollinating plants and eating insects.

Weekly Test 27:

Top-Score Response A top-score response uses details to synthesize and connect ideas about the decline of the reindeer population.

A top-score response should include:
- The reindeer had no natural predators or diseases.
- The reindeer population had grown too large.
- When food became scarce, the reindeer starved to death.

Weekly Test 28:

Top-Score Response A top-score response compares the story of King Midas with the common use of the phrase "Midas touch."

A top-score response should include:
- The "Midas touch" is about creating wealth and good fortune.
- King Midas was able to turn things into gold by touching them.
- A clear definition or example of how the expression is used today.

Weekly Test 29:

Top-Score Response A top-score response should say whether the last sentence is a statement of fact or of opinion, whether or not the student agrees with the statement, and the student's reasons for agreement or disagreement.

A top-score response might include:
- This is a statement of fact because it can be proved that great airships are no longer flying.
- I agree that the great airships are gone forever. They have been replaced by airplanes, then jets, and now rockets and spaceships, and no one will ever travel by airship again.

Weekly Test 30:

Top-Score Response A top-score response correctly tells about Uncle Click's hat and supports an answer about whether the hat got in C.J.'s birthday present by accident or on purpose.

A top-score response should include:
- Uncle Click's hat was with C.J.'s birthday gift.
- A decision about whether Uncle Click put the hat there or it got there by accident.
- Evidence from the text in support of the decision.

VOCABULARY

Directions
Find the word or words with the same meaning as the underlined word. Circle the letter next to the answer.

1 He was not <u>intentionally</u> late.

   A frequently

   (B) purposely

   C accidentally

   D aware

2 She called us <u>insistently</u> while we were away.

   (F) repeatedly

   G one time

   H amazingly

   J loudly

3 My brother <u>grumbled</u> about having to work on Saturday.

   (A) complained

   B ignored

   C worried

   D laughed

4 Chest <u>compressions</u> helped save his life.

   F pulling

   G tightening

   (H) pressing

   J untying

5 Even a <u>minute</u> amount of gold is valuable.

   A very rough

   B very shiny

   C very large

   (D) very small

6 The car was stuck in <u>neutral</u> before it was towed.

   F driving position of the gears

   (G) non-working position of the gears

   H slow position of the gears

   J fast position of the gears

7 Students <u>normally</u> begin school when they are about six years old.

   (A) commonly

   B sometimes

   C never

   D rarely

GO ON

Common Core State Standards

Questions 1–7: **CCSS Language 5.c.** Use the relationship between particular words (e.g., synonyms, antonyms, homographs) to better understand each of the words.

WORD ANALYSIS

Directions Find the word or words with the same meaning as the underlined word. Circle the letter next to the answer.

8 We charged <u>rapidly</u> across the field.

F gracefully

G quickly

C softly

J slowly

9 He returned <u>triumphantly</u> to Rome.

A occasionally

B poorly

C victoriously

D happily

10 We waited <u>patiently</u> for their response.

F angrily

G calmly

H boldly

J sadly

11 The city <u>aggressively</u> defended itself against the attack.

A differently

B greedily

C gently

D forcefully

12 She <u>nervously</u> waited outside the principal's office.

F unsteadily

G quietly

H anxiously

J carefully

COMPREHENSION

Getting into the Game

The coach blew his whistle. Some players ran off the field. Others ran on. Rafael stood watching them.

Rafael was a field goal kicker. He played for his middle school's football team. He was smaller than the other players, but he'd made the team because of his kicking. His legs were strong. He'd lived in South America until last year. Every day after school, he played soccer with friends.

GO ON

Common Core State Standards

Questions 8–12: CCSS Language 4. Determine or clarify the meaning of unknown and multiple-meaning words and phrases based on *grade 5 reading and content,* choosing flexibly from a range of strategies.

He heard the coach's whistle again. Rafael wished he could get into a game. So far, the team had played seven games and had lost them all. He had not yet tried to kick a field goal.

The team hadn't even scored any points. Every time there was a chance, something went wrong. The quarterback threw the ball too high. The running back fumbled. These mistakes bothered the coach. He took their games very seriously.

Sometimes Rafael tried to ask the coach when he might get into a game. The answer was always the same: "Go practice kicking your field goals. We might need you someday." Then the coach walked away. Rafael wasn't sure when the team would need him. There were only two games left.

Just before the last game of the season, Rafael sensed a problem. Some of the other players had lost interest in football. Like him, they stood on the sidelines during games, waiting. The coach called them his "special teams" players. *There was nothing special about them*, Rafael thought. *Except that they were small too.*

After practice, Rafael decided to show the other players how to play soccer. He began dribbling the football like a soccer ball. It rolled end-over-end, but Rafael controlled it skillfully. He kicked it toward another player. "Use your feet," he told him, "but not your hands."

Everybody seemed to be having a good time. It gave Rafael an idea. "You know, we could apply soccer strategies to football," he said. "In soccer, everybody gets to pass. It's not just the quarterback."

Rafael designed a special play. He called it the "Kick Out." It turned the kicker into a quarterback. The kicker threw the ball down the field to another player. That player began running as soon as the ball was snapped.

They practiced the "Kick Out" several times. "It's the greatest play ever!" someone said. Rafael smiled. It made football fun. He knew the team would probably never use his play, but it was good to be prepared.

Directions

Choose the item that best answers each question about the selection you just read. Circle the letter next to the answer.

13 What does Rafael want to do in the story?

Ⓐ play in a football game

B talk to the other players

C make friends

D get stronger

14 Where is Rafael from?

Ⓕ South America

G Europe

H Australia

J Asia

15 How does the coach act toward Rafael?

A He yells at Rafael.

Ⓑ He doesn't want to talk to Rafael.

C He worries about Rafael.

D He makes fun of Rafael.

16 What does Rafael have in common with the other "special teams" players?

F They are related to each other.

G They are friends.

Ⓗ They are small.

J They like football.

17 To help the other players stay interested in football, Rafael teaches them

A how to speak Spanish.

B how to run faster.

C how to kick the ball farther.

Ⓓ how to play soccer.

18 In the special play, what happens as the kicker throws the ball to another player?

F The other players play soccer.

G That player begins guarding.

H The other team tries to kick the ball.

Ⓙ The other team is tricked.

19 What does Rafael call his special play?

Ⓐ the "Kick Out"

B the "Kick Off"

C the "Big Kick"

D the "Kick and Run"

20 For Rafael, the special play at the end of the story shows his

F kicking ability.

G boredom.

H speed.

Ⓙ determination.

GO ON

Common Core State Standards

Questions 13–15, 17–20: CCSS Literature 1. Quote accurately from a text when explaining what the text says explicitly and when drawing inferences from the text. **Question 16: CCSS Literature 3.** Compare and contrast two or more characters, settings, or events in a story or drama, drawing on specific details in the text (e.g., how characters interact).

Name _____

WRITTEN RESPONSE TO THE SELECTION

> **Look Back and Write** Reread the question on page 27. Write an explanation of how Brady helped when others were in danger.

The information in the box below will help you remember what you should think about when you write your composition.

REMEMBER—YOU SHOULD

☐ explain how Brady helped when others were in danger.

☐ use details from the story to support the points you make.

☐ make sure that each sentence you write helps the reader understand your composition.

☐ communicate your ideas clearly so that the reader really understands what you are saying.

☐ check your work for correct spelling, capitalization, punctuation, grammar, and sentences.

Common Core State Standards

CCSS Writing 2. Write informative/explanatory texts to examine a topic and convey ideas and information clearly. (Also **CCSS Writing 4.**, **CCSS Language 1.**, **CCSS Language 2.**)

Weekly Test 1 Unit 1 Week 1

VOCABULARY

*D*irections

Find the word or words with the same meaning as the underlined word. Circle the letter next to the answer.

1 The inside of the cave was the color of <u>pitch</u>.

   A ravens

   B honey

   C shadows

   (D) tar

2 The students learned about <u>veins</u> in science class.

   (F) tubes that carry blood

   G materials that absorb moisture

   H sacks that fill with air

   J threads that connect webs

3 She skipped <u>daintily</u> across the yard.

   A hurriedly

   (B) gracefully

   C promptly

   D constantly

4 The workers <u>constructed</u> the bridge.

   F protected

   G designed

   (H) built

   J avoided

5 The cows had been <u>branded</u>.

   (A) marked

   B released

   C corralled

   D purchased

6 He got into trouble because of his <u>thieving</u>.

   F driving carelessly

   G giving out false information

   (H) taking someone's property

   J responding angrily

7 The accident caused <u>devastation</u>.

   A activity

   (B) destruction

   C concern

   D conversation

GO ON

Common Core State Standards

Questions 1–7: CCSS Language 5.c. Use the relationship between particular words (e.g., synonyms, antonyms, homographs) to better understand each of the words.

WORD ANALYSIS

Directions
Find the word or words with the same meaning as the underlined word. Circle the letter next to the answer.

8 I bought a small <u>figurine</u>.

   F book

   G statue

   H candle

   J fruit

9 The storm caused damage to many <u>structures</u> in town.

   A organizations

   B instructions

   C buildings

   D lives

10 The company <u>imports</u> goods from around the world.

   F brings in

   G builds

   H sells

   J carries out

11 A <u>figure</u> appeared in the distance.

   A color

   B path

   C shape

   D pattern

12 Kenny is shopping for a <u>portable</u> hard drive.

   F secure

   G made by hand

   H cheap

   J easily carried

COMPREHENSION

Del's Butterflies

Del wore a very long face at the breakfast table. It was a Monday morning at the start of summer, and the weather was beautiful. However, Del wouldn't be playing outside or swimming in the community pool today. You see, he was grounded—for a whole week.

"We hate doing this, Del," Mom had explained, "but it's the third time you have taken off for the afternoon without letting us know where you are." It was hard to be sore at Mom . . . but Del really felt sore about this.

GO ON

Common Core State Standards

Questions 8–12: CCSS Language 4.b. Use common, grade-appropriate Greek and Latin affixes and roots as clues to the meaning of a word or phrase.

After breakfast Mom said, "Cheer up, Del. You should look at this week as an opportunity to learn some new things about yourself."

Del did not find this speech at all convincing. He went out the back door and flopped on the bench in Mom's garden. *A good place to mope*, Del thought.

Suddenly, a spot of color in the corner of his eye caught his attention. Del turned his head sharply. There, as big as a kite, was a butterfly with yellow wings.

"Mom!" shouted Del. "I just saw the most beautiful butterfly!"

At once, Mom came out the back door and said, "What did you see, Del?" As Del talked, Mom nodded her head and said, "That's a tiger swallowtail. I've planted flowers and shrubs that attract butterflies, and I'm sure you'll see many more varieties if you pay attention. Say, that nice Mr. Lopez next door used to be an entomologist—an insect scientist—before he retired. I bet he could share some useful information with you. I'll give him a call."

Minutes later, Mom brought Mr. Lopez out into the garden. As he handed a pile of books to Del, Mr. Lopez said, "These will help you identify your butterflies, Del. I also have a kit for capturing butterflies."

"Thanks, Mr. Lopez," said Del, "but that sounds kind of mean. I think I'll stick to photographing them."

After Mr. Lopez left, Del armed himself with his camera and butterfly books. Every so often, Mom would hear yelling from the garden, such as, "That's a red admiral," or, "I just saw a monarch!"

The week flew by. By Saturday Del had found fifteen kinds of butterflies, and he had pictures to prove it!

"Del, I have an idea," said Mom. "Let's make a book of the butterflies you have found. I think the county museum might be interested in your work."

"Cool!" piped Del.

Directions

Choose the item that best answers each question about the selection you just read. Circle the letter next to the answer.

13 Why is Del upset with his mother at the beginning of the story?

  A She forgot it was his birthday.

  B She told him he had to make his own breakfast.

  (C) She has grounded him.

  D She won't let him play soccer.

14 What is the cause of Del's being grounded for a whole week?

  F He got a bad grade in math.

  G He stayed out too late.

  H He did not do his chores for several days.

  (J) He didn't let his parents know where he was going.

15 After breakfast, Del goes

  A to school.

  (B) into the garden.

  C to his room.

  D to the basement.

16 What happens as a result of Del calling to his mother?

  F Mr. Lopez drops by to visit.

  G His mother gets frightened.

  H Del is grounded for a week.

  (J) His mother comes out into the garden.

17 Why is Del's backyard full of butterflies?

  A It's been a hot summer with lots of rain.

  (B) Del's mother has planted flowers to attract butterflies.

  C The insects are attracted to the color that the house is painted.

  D His next-door neighbor studies insects.

18 Why does Mr. Lopez come to visit Del?

  F He thinks that Del has knocked down his bird feeder.

  G He is tutoring Del in science.

  (H) Del's mother asks him to talk to Del about butterflies.

  J He wants to wish Del a happy birthday.

19 Del politely refuses Mr. Lopez's offer of the kit for capturing butterflies because

  (A) he does not want to hurt them.

  B he strongly dislikes Mr. Lopez.

  C his mother doesn't want him to take it.

  D he doesn't think that Mr. Lopez is serious about his offer.

20 Which word best describes Del's mother?

  (F) sympathetic

  G uncaring

  H distracted

  J selfish

GO ON

Common Core State Standards

Questions 13–20: CCSS Literature 1. Quote accurately from a text when explaining what the text says explicitly and when drawing inferences from the text.

WRITTEN RESPONSE TO THE SELECTION

> **Look Back and Write** Reread the question on page 57. Think about one challenge Rose set for herself. Write an explanation of how she faced that challenge.

The information in the box below will help you remember what you should think about when you write your composition.

REMEMBER—YOU SHOULD

☐ explain how Rose faced the challenge she set for herself.

☐ make sure you use descriptive words that engage the reader.

☐ use time-order words when you describe events in sequence.

☐ use details from the story to support your explanation.

☐ check your work for correct spelling, capitalization, punctuation, grammar, and sentences.

GO ON

Common Core State Standards

CCSS Writing 2. Write informative/explanatory texts to examine a topic and convey ideas and information clearly. (Also **CCSS Writing 9.**)

_____

_____

_____

_____

_____

_____

_____

_____

_____

_____

_____

_____

_____

_____

_____

_____

_____

_____

_____

VOCABULARY

Directions
Find the word or words with the same meaning as the underlined word. Circle the letter next to the answer.

1 The tourists went to the <u>headland</u>.

   A land on top of a cliff

   B land surrounded by wild grasses

   C land that sticks out into the sea

   D land covered with rocks

2 We saw many <u>shellfish</u> during our visit.

   F sea creatures

   G beach pebbles

   H water birds

   J river stones

3 The hiker found a <u>lair</u>.

   A decayed tusk

   B forgotten trail

   C ground nest

   D animal's den

4 The dog <u>gnawed</u> the stick.

   F fetched

   G chewed

   H ignored

   J dodged

5 The water was full of <u>kelp</u>.

   A small reptiles

   B flowing lava

   C sea plants

   D bright coral

6 Her moccasins were made with real <u>sinew</u>.

   F antlers

   G cord connecting muscle and bone

   H minerals

   J thread made from sheepskin

7 A creek flowed through the <u>ravine</u>.

   A distant mountains

   B dark cave

   C dense forest

   D deep valley

GO ON

Common Core State Standards

Questions 1–7: CCSS Language 5.c. Use the relationship between particular words (e.g., synonyms, antonyms, homographs) to better understand each of the words.

WORD ANALYSIS

Directions
Find the compound word in each sentence. Circle the letter next to the answer.

8 I am writing a letter to the local newspaper persuading people to recycle.

(F) newspaper

G recycle

H persuading

J writing

9 To prevent an accident, make sure you only cross the street at a crosswalk.

A accident

B street

(C) crosswalk

D prevent

10 She needs to purchase a new keyboard for her computer.

F computer

(G) keyboard

H purchase

J needs

11 James is busily constructing a workshop with his father.

A busily

(B) workshop

C father

D constructing

12 The fish was so huge that Jamie almost fell overboard trying to reel it in!

F reel

G trying

H almost

(J) overboard

GO ON

Common Core State Standards

Questions 8–12: CCSS Foundational Skills 3.a. Use combined knowledge of all letter-sound correspondences, syllabication patterns, and morphology (e.g., roots and affixes) to read accurately unfamiliar multisyllabic words in context and out of context.

COMPREHENSION

Will's Sharp Eye

It was the spring of 1822, and Will Carter was a hard-working teenager, nearly 17 years old. The Carters had a farm near town, and Will worked in Mr. Benson's store part-time. James Benson was a merchant in the growing town of Madison, Indiana. He was looking for a strong lad to help his oldest son, Tom, take a flatboat down to New Orleans.

Farmers could raise a lot of crops on the fertile soil of southern Indiana, but getting their goods to market was difficult. Back in 1822, there were no railroads or paved highways. The best route was by boat down the Ohio River and then down the Mississippi River, all the way to the big, bustling port of New Orleans. To ship their goods, people built flatboats—big, floating, wooden boxes that strong, young fellows like Tom Benson and Will Carter could push and pull down the rivers with poles shaped like giant oars. In April of 1822, Tom and Will eagerly pushed off from Madison's riverbank.

Sure, there was work to do on the boat, but a lot of the time was taken up with just being idle. Will took in all the sights. He loved the birds that flocked to and fro near the rivers. He watched ducks and herons near the shores, close to the water. Where steeps bluffs crowded the river's edge, he spied eagles and falcons soaring high above. Will didn't miss much that was worth seeing.

One warm, lazy afternoon, the flatboat was riding a good current down the Mississippi, and the two boys were enjoying the ride. "This is the life," said Tom. "Don't you agree, Will?"

Will was about to answer, but just then his eye caught sight of something mean sticking up out of the river not far ahead. "Snag in the water!" he shouted. That instant, Tom bolted to take his position at his steering pole; Will was already at his. The two boys deftly edged the boat out of the current, passing to the left of the drowned tree trunk.

"Whew! That was close," said Will. "We make a pretty good team, don't we?"

"Thanks to your eagle eye, Will, we came through all right," said Tom. "I've heard stories about folks who get capsized by snags in the river. And that was really a big one!"

The boys had some more adventures before they got down to New Orleans. But they delivered their goods as promised and made it safely back home to Indiana.

GO ON

Directions

Choose the item that best answers each question about the reading selection. Circle the letter next to the answer.

13 Where does the story start?

A in New Orleans, Louisiana

B on the Ohio River

C on the Mississippi River

(D) in Madison, Indiana

14 Where does most of the story take place?

F at the market in New Orleans

G on the Carters' farm in Indiana

(H) on the flatboat on the rivers

J in Mr. Benson's store in Indiana

15 What word best describes the relationship between Will and Tom?

A strangers

B enemies

(C) friends

D opponents

16 What does Tom do when Will calls out about the snag?

F He refuses to believe it.

(G) He rushes to his steering pole.

H He remains lying down.

J He watches the birds near the shores.

17 What is one theme of this story?

(A) Teamwork has benefits.

B Pioneers had a hard life.

C The world is full of beautiful things.

D There is always competition between young men.

18 Which word or phrase best describes Will?

F lazy and easily bored

G sly and untrustworthy

(H) watchful and quick on his feet

J slow-witted

19 Why did many merchants in the 1800s take the trouble to send flatboats down the rivers?

A There were no risks or dangers on the rivers.

B The Indians controlled all the land routes.

C The merchants received tax discounts for flatboats.

(D) There were no railroads, airplanes, or good highways.

20 Which is a possible theme of this story?

F Only one person can be in charge.

G Rivers are a peaceful way to travel.

H Doing your work quickly is the most important thing.

(J) Always be ready for action.

GO ON

> **Common Core State Standards**

Questions 13–16, 18–19: CCSS Literature 1. Quote accurately from a text when explaining what the text says explicitly and when drawing inferences from the text. **Questions 17, 20: CCSS Literature 2.** Determine a theme of a story, drama, or poem from details in the text, including how characters in a story or drama respond to challenges or how the speaker in a poem reflects upon a topic; summarize the text.

WRITTEN RESPONSE TO THE SELECTION

> **Look Back and Write** Look back at page 97. Cutting poles for a house was physically challenging for Karana. How did she meet this challenge?

The information in the box below will help you remember what you should think about when you write your composition.

REMEMBER—YOU SHOULD

☐ explain how Karana met the challenge of cutting poles for a house.

☐ make sure you include all the steps involved in the process.

☐ use details from the story to support your explanation.

☐ communicate your ideas clearly so that the reader really understands what you are saying.

☐ check your work for correct spelling, capitalization, punctuation, grammar, and sentences.

GO ON

Common Core State Standards

CCSS Writing 2. Write informative/explanatory texts to examine a topic and convey ideas and information clearly. (Also **CCSS Writing 2.a.,** **CCSS Writing 2.b., CCSS Writing 4., CCSS Language 1.**)

VOCABULARY

Directions Find the word or words with the same meaning as the underlined word. Circle the letter next to the answer.

1 Her handwriting is <u>unique</u>.

   A dainty

   (B) special

   C sloppy

   D acceptable

2 He has a lot of <u>confidence</u>.

   F well-developed skills

   G selfish thoughts

   H charming manners

   (J) sureness of his abilities

3 Kay enjoys playing in the <u>outfield</u>.

   A part of the baseball field closest to home plate

   B the mound that the pitcher stands on

   (C) part of the baseball field farthest from the batter

   D shelter containing the players' bench

4 He answered her in a <u>mocking</u> voice.

   F playful

   G harsh

   (H) insulting

   J demanding

5 In the performance, singing was his <u>weakness</u>.

   (A) least-developed skill

   B cause for celebration

   C main purpose

   D reason for feeling breathless

6 The crowd was silent during the <u>windup</u>.

   F announcement of the lineup

   (G) pitcher's movements before pitching the ball

   H coach's signals to his players

   J entrance of the players onto the field

7 She had a good <u>fastball</u>.

   A a pitch thrown with a spin

   B a pitch thrown with a wet ball

   C a pitch thrown outside the strike zone

   (D) a pitch thrown at full speed

GO ON

Common Core State Standards

Questions 1–7: CCSS Language 5.c. Use the relationship between particular words (e.g., synonyms, antonyms, homographs) to better understand each of the words.

WORD ANALYSIS

Directions
Find the word or words with the closest meaning to the underlined word. Circle the letter next to the answer.

8 Only a small flow of water was in the <u>creek</u>.

   (F) little stream

   G heavy flood

   H light trickle

   J river

9 After not getting enough sleep, Kyle woke up in a <u>grumpy</u> mood.

   A angry

   B horrible

   C unkind

   (D) crabby

10 I loved the art exhibit, but my brother thought it was <u>dull</u>.

   F worn down

   G lifeless

   H lacking color

   (J) boring

11 The <u>gigantic</u> statue towered over the park.

   A big

   B vast

   (C) enormous

   D extensive

12 Trina was <u>sobbing</u> by the end of the movie.

   F having tears in your eyes

   (G) bawling

   H whimpering softly

   J sniffling

GO ON

Common Core State Standards

Questions 8–12: CCSS Language 5.c. Use the relationship between particular words (e.g., synonyms, antonyms, homographs) to better understand each of the words.

COMPREHENSION
The Great Babe Didrikson

Who was the greatest woman athlete of all time? Many people think it was Babe Didrikson. She played more sports and was better at them than almost anyone else. Although she died more than fifty years ago at the peak of her career, the great Babe Didrikson is not forgotten.

Babe was born in 1911 in Port Arthur, Texas. Her parents had come to the United States from Norway to find a better life. When Babe was little, her family moved to Beaumont, Texas, to get farther away from the coast. That's because a powerful hurricane struck Port Arthur in 1914 and took many lives.

Babe's real name was Mildred, but her childhood friends gave her the nickname "Babe," comparing her to Babe Ruth. In the 1920s, everyone in America knew that Babe Ruth was the king of baseball. Well, "Babe" Didrikson could hit lots of home runs too!

Babe aced every sport she attempted. Her body was perfect for sports—short and trim with lean, strong muscles. In 1932, Babe made the United States Olympic team. In the Los Angeles Olympics that year, she won gold medals for javelin throwing and for hurdles, and she broke some world records too.

After the Olympics, Babe began playing golf. Of course, she was great at golf—just like every other sport. At that time, few women played golf. Babe Didrikson led the way. She helped form the Ladies' Professional Golf Association, or LPGA for short; meanwhile, she won trophy after trophy. Her best years were in the late 1940s and early 1950s. In 1948, she won a "grand slam"—three major tournaments in one year. In all, she won eighty-two golf tournaments.

Babe had many other talents too. As a young woman, she sang and played the harmonica and even made a music recording. In later years, she sewed her own clothes for her golf tournaments.

In 1938, Babe married George Zaharias, who was also a famous athlete. Mr. and Mrs. Zaharias had a lot in common—their love of sports.

In 1999, the Associated Press and *Sports Illustrated* magazine named Babe Didrikson the woman athlete of the century. That was forty-three years after her death in 1956. Today you can visit the Babe Didrikson Zaharias Museum in Beaumont, Texas.

GO ON

Directions

Choose the item that best answers each question about the reading selection. Circle the letter next to the answer.

13 Which of the following is a statement of fact?

- A She was better at sports than almost anyone else.
- **B** Babe was born in Port Arthur, Texas.
- C Her body was perfect for sports.
- D Of course, she was great at golf.

14 Which statement can't be proved by checking a reference source?

- F When Babe was little, her family moved to Beaumont, Texas.
- G 1n 1932, Babe made the United States Olympic team.
- **H** The great Babe Didrikson is not forgotten.
- J In 1938, Babe married George Zaharias.

15 Which is a statement of opinion?

- **A** Babe Didrikson was the greatest woman athlete of all time.
- B A powerful hurricane struck Port Arthur in 1914.
- C Babe won gold medals for javelin and hurdles.
- D The Babe Didrikson Zaharias museum is in Beaumont, Texas.

16 Why did the Didrikson family move away from Port Arthur?

- **F** They wanted to live farther from the coast.
- G They wanted to return to Norway.
- H Babe married George Zaharias.
- J Their daughter Babe was a great athlete.

17 When was Babe born?

- A 1899
- **B** 1911
- C 1914
- D 1932

18 For what sports did Babe win gold medals at the 1932 Los Angeles Olympics?

- F golf and field hockey
- **G** javelin throwing and hurdles
- H tennis and racquet ball
- J swimming and track

19 Which of the following contains a statement of opinion?

- A After the Olympics, Babe Didrikson began playing golf.
- B In 1948, Babe won a Grand Slam—three major golf tournaments.
- C Babe sewed her own clothes for her golf tournaments.
- **D** She played more sports and was better at them than almost anyone else.

20 Which of the following events happened last?

- F Babe got married.
- G Babe's family moved to Beaumont, Texas.
- **H** Babe was voted woman athlete of the century.
- J Babe played in the 1932 Olympics.

GO ON

Common Core State Standards

Questions 13–20: CCSS Informational Text 1. Quote accurately from a text when explaining what the text says explicitly and when drawing inferences from the text.

WRITTEN RESPONSE TO THE SELECTION

Look Back and Write Look back at page 128. What is the "typical Satch style" that the author is referring to?

The information in the box below will help you remember what you should think about when you write your composition.

REMEMBER—YOU SHOULD

☐ explain what the "typical Satch style" is that the author refers to.

☐ refer to both Satchel Page's words and actions in your answer.

☐ support your points with details from the text.

☐ organize your ideas in a logical manner so that the reader understands what you are saying.

☐ check your work for correct spelling, capitalization, punctuation, grammar, and sentences.

Common Core State Standards

CCSS Writing 2.b. Develop the topic with facts, definitions, concrete details, quotations, or other information and examples related to the topic. (Also **CCSS Writing 2.c., CCSS Language 1., CCSS Language 3.a.**)

_____

_____

_____

_____

_____

_____

_____

_____

_____

_____

_____

_____

_____

_____

_____

_____

_____

_____

_____

_____

_____

_____

VOCABULARY

Directions
Find the word or words with the same meaning as the underlined word. Circle the letter next to the answer.

1 The roar of the airplane was <u>deafening</u>.

   A very soft

   B far away

   C very loud

   D close by

2 His <u>prying</u> eyes made people uncomfortable.

   F inquiring

   G large

   H sad

   J cloudy

3 The subway car <u>lurched</u> from side to side.

   A stopped slowly

   B rolled suddenly

   C sped up quickly

   D went in reverse

4 The new house stands where a <u>previous</u> cottage once did.

   F larger

   G later

   H smaller

   J earlier

5 She enjoys hiking to the top of the mountain and <u>surveying</u> the valley.

   A writing about

   B looking carefully at

   C painting pictures of

   D thinking about

6 The disease killed many trees and made others <u>barren</u>.

   F unable to produce fruit

   G needing a shady spot

   H unable to find water

   J needing strong sunlight

GO ON

Common Core State Standards

Questions 1–6: CCSS Language 5.c. Use the relationship between particular words (e.g., synonyms, antonyms, homographs) to better understand each of the words.

WORD ANALYSIS

D*irections*
Find the word or words with the same meaning as the underlined word. Circle the letter next to the answer.

7 The storekeeper was <u>reporting</u> the crime.

  A watching

  (B) telling about

  C helping

  D ignoring

8 The lawyer was busy <u>presenting</u> the case.

  F wrapping

  G finishing

  (H) stating

  J joking about

9 Marie is <u>designing</u> three new dresses for her spring collection.

  (A) making plans to create

  B borrowing

  C preparing to sell

  D getting rid of

10 The men were <u>laboring</u> all day in the sun.

  F tanning

  (G) working

  H resting

  J playing

11 Devon started <u>believing</u> in the importance of education when he saw how successful it made him.

  A feeling unsure of a position

  (B) having a strong devotion to a cause

  C having a mild interest in a subject

  D taking careful consideration of an issue

12 The radio talk show host thanked the caller for <u>listening</u>.

  (F) hearing the show

  G enjoying art

  H sharing ideas

  J being political

COMPREHENSION

Telling Time: Early Calendars and Clocks

People have measured time for thousands of years. Before there were clocks, people used the sun, the moon, and the stars to tell time. Ancient peoples did not keep track of time the same way we do today. They did not get up at the same time every morning for school or work. Time was a small—but important—part of their lives for other reasons.

The first people to measure small units of time were the Sumerians. Roughly five thousand years ago, they created a calendar that divided a year into twelve months of thirty days each. The calendar also divided each day into twelve–hour parts. Each part was further divided into thirty more parts. This calendar was based on the movements of the sun.

GO ON

> **Common Core State Standards**

Questions 7–12: CCSS Language 4.a. Use context (e.g., cause/effect relationships and comparisons in text) as a clue to the meaning of a word or phrase.

Egyptians were the next people to measure time. They based their calendar on the moon's cycles. However, every time the Nile River flooded, they realized that a certain star called Sirius rose next to the sun. This happened every 365 days. It convinced the Egyptians to switch to a 365-day calendar.

As their calendar improved, Egyptians began making early clocks to measure time further. The clocks used elements from the natural world such as sunlight, shadows, and water. Egyptian clocks helped people organize their time. They also divided time into smaller and smaller parts.

The first of these new clocks were called sun clocks. They were tall and thin with four sides. Shadows moving across the surface divided the day into sections similar to hours. Sun clocks also worked as calendars. When the shadow cast at noon was at its longest, Egyptians knew that it was the shortest day of the year (and vice versa).

Sundials were invented next. They measured hours better by using stone columns to divide a day into twelve parts. When the sun shone on top of a column, its shadow told how much daylight was left. Sundials worked well, but they were ineffective on cloudy and rainy days when there was little sunshine. Sundials helped Egyptians track the growing seasons and know when rain was coming.

Then the Egyptians developed water clocks. They made them from stone bowls with sloped sides. As water dripped steadily through a small hole near the bottom, markings on the inside of the bowl showed time passing. Water clocks were helpful because they worked while people were sleeping. Some water clocks were silent. Others opened doors or windows to show figures. These clocks later influenced cuckoo clocks in the eighteenth and nineteenth centuries. Cuckoo clocks came with figures of African cuckoo birds in them. The birds popped out at the beginning of every hour to signal the time.

Civilization or Era	Device(s) Used to Measure Time
Prehistoric	position of stars in the sky
Sumerian	12-month 360-day solar calendar 12-hour day
Egyptian	365-day lunar calendar sun clock sundial water clock
18th–19th centuries	cuckoo clocks

Directions

Choose the item that best answers each question about the selection you just read. Circle the letter next to the answer.

13 Before clocks, people measured time by using objects found in the

(A) sky.

B ground.

C water.

D air.

14 The sun's movements helped ancient Sumerians create the first

F sun clocks.

G water clocks.

H sundials.

(J) calendars.

15 Egyptians changed to a 365-day calendar because, once every 365 days,

A the river god got angry.

(B) the Nile River flooded.

C the rainy season started.

D the sun came out.

16 Egyptians knew when it was the longest day of the year because

(F) the shadow on the sun clock was shortest.

G the shadow on the sun clock was longest.

H there were no shadows on the sun clock.

J there were more than twelve shadows on the sun clock.

17 The chart at the end of the selection shows that sundials were invented

A by prehistoric peoples.

B by the Sumerians.

(C) by the Egyptians.

D in the eighteenth century.

18 Why were water clocks so useful?

F They told the length of the growing season.

(G) They told the time at night.

H They told the time of the rainy season.

J They told the time in the desert.

19 The figures in early water clocks later caused the invention of

A sundials.

B water clocks.

(C) cuckoo clocks.

D African birds.

20 What is the main idea of this passage?

F Ancient peoples liked looking at the sun and the moon.

(G) Ancient peoples found creative ways to tell time.

H Ancient peoples liked building clocks.

J Ancient peoples were not interested in telling time.

GO ON

Common Core State Standards

Questions 13–16, 18–19: CCSS Informational Text 3. Explain the relationships or interactions between two or more individuals, events, ideas, or concepts in a historical, scientific, or technical text based on specific information in the text. **Question 17: CCSS Informational Text 7.** Draw on information from multiple print or digital sources, demonstrating the ability to locate an answer to a question quickly or to solve a problem efficiently. **Question 20: CCSS Informational Text 2.** Determine two or more main ideas of a text and explain how they are supported by key details; summarize the text.

WRITTEN RESPONSE TO THE SELECTION

> **Look Back and Write** Explain in your own words how the railroad crew managed to lay ten miles of track in one day.

The information in the box below will help you remember what you should think about when you write your composition.

REMEMBER—YOU SHOULD

☐   explain how the railroad crew managed to lay ten miles of track in one day.

☐   make sure to use your own words in your composition.

☐   summarize events in the text as you write, focusing on the important detail.

☐   describe the events in the sequence in which they occurred.

☐   check your work for correct spelling, capitalization, punctuation, grammar, and sentences.

⌐ **Common Core State Standards** ⌐

CCSS Writing 2.b. Develop the topic with facts, definitions, concrete details, quotations, or other information and examples related to the topic. (Also **CCSS Informational Text 1., CCSS Language 1., CCSS Writing 2.a., CCSS Writing 4.**)

_____

_____

_____

_____

_____

_____

_____

_____

_____

_____

_____

_____

_____

_____

_____

_____

_____

_____

_____

_____

VOCABULARY

Directions

Find the word or words with the same meaning as the underlined word. Circle the letter next to the answer.

1 The students looked at the <u>algae</u> under the microscope.

　Ⓐ simple plants

　B small fish

　C sea urchins

　D crystals

2 He collected <u>driftwood</u>.

　F wood used by artists

　G wood from evergreen trees

　H wood that is strong and heavy

　Ⓙ wood that washes up on shore

3 She can't find the <u>tweezers</u>.

　A a device used for cutting

　B small tubes used to curl hair

　C cloth coverings for the hands

　Ⓓ small metal tool used for plucking

4 He <u>lamented</u> the price of gasoline.

　F kept a record of

　G reduced

　Ⓗ expressed sadness about

　J liked

5 The gifts for her were <u>concealed</u>.

　Ⓐ hidden

　B expensive

　C astonishing

　D purchased

6 She talked to the dog <u>sternly</u>.

　F uneasily

　Ⓖ harshly

　H frantically

　J adoringly

7 He got a new <u>hammock</u>.

　A small hammer

　Ⓑ hanging bed

　C storage pouch

　D cloth shelter

GO ON

Common Core State Standards

Questions 1–7: CCSS Language 5.c. Use the relationship between particular words (e.g., synonyms, antonyms, homographs) to better understand each of the words.

WORD ANALYSIS   OPTIONAL SUBTEST

*D*irections
Find the word or words with the same meaning as the underlined word. Circle the letter next to the answer.

8 She ate lunch in the <u>cabana</u> by the pool.

   F cafeteria

   (G) small shelter

   H lifeguard station

   J reclining chair

9 We enjoyed the <u>tortillas</u> my grandmother had made.

   (A) thin, round flat cakes

   B things shaped like hard-shelled animals

   C small, ring-shaped stuffed pasta

   D laws

10 The powerful <u>hurricane</u> is getting closer to Florida.

   F freighter

   (G) ocean storm

   H military aircraft

   J heat wave

11 Many early cultures relied on <u>maize</u> as a source of food.

   A wheat

   B soybeans

   C rice

   (D) corn

12 The hikers descended into the deep <u>canyon</u>.

   F underground cave

   G bottomless pit

   (H) narrow valley

   J empty grassland

COMPREHENSION

The Youngest Fireman

Dave Duncan looked outside. It was another hot day. The forest was quiet. There wasn't even a breeze.

Dave was a forest ranger. He was in charge of spotting fires in a large state forest. He knew that rangers used to sit in fire towers and look for smoke. But Dave's job was different. He worked in an office at a ranger station. He monitored cameras placed at several locations throughout the forest.

Dave's son Danny walked into his office. "Hi, Dad," he said. "What are you doing?" Danny was twelve and tall for his age. He was nearly the same height as his father.

GO ON

> **Common Core State Standards**

Questions 8–12: CCSS Language 5.c. Use the relationship between particular words (e.g., synonyms, antonyms, homographs) to better understand each of the words.

Dave smiled. "The usual," he replied. "But there's nothing new to report." Dave and Danny had been living at the ranger station for almost a month. They were far from civilization, and Dave liked how peaceful things were. Danny was getting bored, though. In less than two weeks, he would be going back to school.

"Want to go for a walk outside?" Danny asked eagerly. He liked to get out of the station, which was small. Dave didn't go out much, though. The summer had been dry, and fires were likely. If Dave saw smoke on a camera, he needed to alert the other rangers.

"Maybe a little later," Dave said. "After I finish—" Suddenly an alarm began going off. Dave's eyes widened. Danny looked nervously at his father.

"What is it?" he asked. "Is there a fire somewhere?"

"Yes," Dave told him, "But it's here in the ranger station. We have to get out now!" Dave grabbed Danny's hand. They raced out of the building. Smoke poured out of a basement window. Dave felt for the two-way radio normally clipped to his belt. It wasn't there. "I have to go back in," he told Danny. "I left my radio on the table. We need it to call for help!"

Danny didn't want to let go of his father's hand. "You can't," he told him. "It's too dangerous!"

"I'll be right back," Dave said. "Don't worry." He ran back into the smoky building.

Just then Danny remembered seeing a garden hose outside the station. He had cooled himself off with it last week. Quickly he turned on the water full blast and aimed the spray at the basement window.

Dave came back and saw Danny with the hose. The flames were almost out. "The fire department will be here soon," he told his son. "But it looks like we won't need them. Good job—you're the youngest fireman I know!"

GO ON

Directions
Choose the item that best answers each question about the selection you just read. Circle the letter next to the answer.

13 Why did the author include paragraph 2 in the story?

A to give background on the forest

B to show Dave and Danny's relationship

C to describe the ranger station

(D) to show how Dave is different from other rangers

14 Dave and Danny are almost the same

(F) height.

G shirt size.

H age.

J shoe size.

15 Which of the following statements best describes a difference between Dave and Danny?

A Dave likes cameras, but Danny doesn't.

(B) Danny wants to go outside, but Dave doesn't.

C Dave wants to go outside, but Danny doesn't.

D Danny likes to listen to the radio, but Dave doesn't.

16 During which season does the story take place?

(F) summer

G winter

H spring

J fall

17 Living in the ranger station, Dave and Danny could best be compared to

A workers in a factory.

B students at a school.

(C) soldiers on guard duty.

D players on a sports team.

18 What makes the fire that Danny fights different from other forest fires?

F There is no smoke.

G It starts in a tree.

H It spreads quickly.

(J) It is in the ranger station.

19 What does Danny use to fight the fire?

A a fire hydrant

B a shovel

(C) a hose

D a two-way radio

20 In paragraph 10, the author shows Dave's

F sense of humor.

G boredom.

(H) courage.

J athletic ability.

GO ON

Common Core State Standards

Questions 13, 16–19: CCSS Literature 1. Quote accurately from a text when explaining what the text says explicitly and when drawing inferences from the text. Questions 14–15: CCSS Literature 3. Compare and contrast two or more characters, settings, or events in a story or drama, drawing on specific details in the text (e.g., how characters interact). Question 20: CCSS Literature 2. Determine a theme of a story, drama, or poem from details in the text, including how characters in a story or drama respond to challenges or how the speaker in a poem reflects upon a topic; summarize the text.

WRITTEN RESPONSE TO THE SELECTION

> **Look Back and Write** Look back at page 193. Explain in your own words what led Fernando to confess.

The information in the box below will help you remember what you should think about when you write your composition.

REMEMBER—YOU SHOULD

☐　explain what led Fernando to confess.

☐　use your own words to answer the question.

☐　use details from the story to support your ideas.

☐　communicate your ideas clearly so that the reader really understands what you are saying.

☐　check your work for correct spelling, capitalization, punctuation, grammar, and sentences.

GO ON

Common Core State Standards

CCSS Writing 3.b. Use narrative techniques, such as dialogue, description, and pacing, to develop experiences and events or show the responses of characters to situations. (Also **CCSS Literature 1., CCSS Language 1., CCSS Language 3., CCSS Writing 3.**)

_____

_____

_____

_____

_____

_____

_____

_____

_____

_____

_____

_____

_____

_____

_____

_____

_____

_____

_____

_____

_____

VOCABULARY

Directions

Find the word or words with the same meaning as the underlined word. Circle the letter next to the answer.

1 The people staged a <u>rebellion</u> against the king.

   A joyful festival

   B peaceful protest

   C petty argument

   (D) armed uprising

2 I did not want to join the <u>confederacy</u>.

   (F) league

   G team

   H journey

   J company

3 The winning athletes basked in <u>glory</u>.

   A victory

   B warm water

   (C) honor

   D love

4 The workers formed a <u>union</u> for their mutual protection.

   F collection

   (G) alliance

   H gathering

   J marriage

5 I offered the <u>stallion</u> an apple.

   (A) horse

   B dog

   C rooster

   D bull

6 I slung my <u>canteen</u> over my shoulder.

   (F) pouch that holds water

   G suitcase that holds clothing

   H purse that holds money

   J briefcase that holds papers

7 The twins began to <u>quarrel</u>.

   A play

   B sing

   (C) argue

   D sleep

GO ON

> **Common Core State Standards**

Questions 1–7: CCSS Language 5.c. Use the relationship between particular words (e.g., synonyms, antonyms, homographs) to better understand each of the words.

WORD ANALYSIS

Directions
Find the word or words with the same meaning as the underlined word. Circle the letter next to the answer.

8 The exchange student received a <u>visa</u>.

   F airline ticket

   G photo book

   H birthday card

   (J) passport stamp

9 You should not <u>disguise</u> your true feelings.

   A expose

   B confuse

   C dress up

   (D) conceal

10 Have you been to the new <u>restaurant</u> in town?

   (F) a place to eat

   G a place to sleep

   H a place to shop

   J a place to rest

11 That is a beautiful <u>bouquet</u> of flowers!

   A color

   (B) arrangement

   C field

   D painting

12 We kept the seashell from the beach as a <u>souvenir</u>.

   F example

   G choice

   (H) memento

   J gift

GO ON

Common Core State Standards

Questions 8–12: CCSS Language 5.c. Use the relationship between particular words (e.g., synonyms, antonyms, homographs) to better understand each of the words.

COMPREHENSION
Sylvia Earle—Ocean Explorer

Sylvia Earle was born in 1935. Her parents took her to the beach when she was little. She saw crabs and other animals that live in the ocean. She started writing down notes about them.

When Sylvia was thirteen, her family moved to Florida. They lived near the beach. She saw starfish and many other interesting types of sea life. She watched them closely.

In 1952, Sylvia went to college. Afterward, she started studying the plants and animals that live in the ocean. Then she got married and started a family.

In 1964, a group of scientists asked her to go on a research trip to the Indian Ocean. At the time, it was unusual for women to go on scientific trips. Sylvia went on the trip even though her children were very young. During the next few years, she went on more trips. In 1970, she led a team of women scientists that lived for two weeks in a small city. It was fifty feet underwater!

In the 1970s, Dr. Earle had many adventures. She followed sperm whales and went on research trips to New Zealand, Australia, South Africa, and Alaska. In 1979, she walked on the ocean floor off the coast of Hawaii. The depth was 1,250 feet. No one has walked deeper in the ocean since.

In the 1980s, she began studying animals, such as giant squids, that live in the deepest parts of the ocean. She also helped design a small submarine called Deep Rover. Dr. Earle used this submarine to go 3,300 feet below the ocean's surface. Her dives and her work on Deep Rover earned her the nickname "Her Deepness."

Today, she is one of the most famous women scientists in the world. She is also an Explorer-in-Residence at the National Geographic Society. Her children, who are now grown up, sometimes help her with her work. She tries to teach people about the wonders of the world's oceans.

Dr. Earle also thinks it is very important to protect the oceans from pollution and other dangers. Scientists still do not understand many things about different types of sea life. Dr. Earle hopes future scientists will keep studying the oceans and uncover more secrets.

GO ON

Directions

Choose the item that best answers each question about the selection you just read. Circle the letter next to the answer.

13 Which event takes place first?

A Sylvia goes on a trip to the Indian Ocean.

(B) Sylvia goes to college.

C Sylvia has a family.

D Sylvia designs a submarine.

14 The information presented in this passage is mainly organized

F by comparing and contrasting.

(G) in chronological order.

H by cause and effect.

J with main ideas and support.

15 Why did the author include paragraph 4 in the passage?

A to show why Sylvia Earle began studying sperm whales

B to show where Sylvia Earle went to college

(C) to show how Sylvia Earle began doing scientific research

D to show when Sylvia Earle started working for the National Geographic Society

16 How did Dr. Earle earn the nickname "Her Deepness"?

(F) by walking on the ocean floor and diving in a submarine

G by studying sea life

H by teaching people about the ocean

J by following whales from New Zealand to Alaska

17 In which decade did Sylvia help design a small submarine?

A 1950s

B 1960s

C 1970s

(D) 1980s

18 In what year did Sylvia Earle live underwater for two weeks?

F 1935

G 1964

(H) 1970

J 1979

19 What made Sylvia different from most other scientists who went on research trips in the 1960s?

(A) She was a woman and had young children.

B She had always been curious about ocean life.

C She worked for the National Geographic Society.

D She was from Florida.

20 When did Sylvia set a record for depth in undersea walking?

F 1952

G 1964

(H) 1979

J 1982

GO ON

Common Core State Standards

Questions 13, 19: CCSS Informational Text 3. Explain the relationships or interactions between two or more individuals, events, ideas, or concepts in a historical, scientific, or technical text based on specific information in the text. **Questions 14–16, 17–18, 20: CCSS Informational Text 1.** Quote accurately from a text when explaining what the text says explicitly and when drawing inferences from the text.

WRITTEN RESPONSE TO THE SELECTION

> **Look Back and Write** Look back at the Epilogue on page 219. Why was William H. Carney awarded the Congressional Medal of Honor? Why was this a special achievement?

The information in the box below will help you remember what you should think about when you write your composition.

REMEMBER—YOU SHOULD

☐ explain why William H. Carney was awarded the Congressional Medal of Honor and why this was a special achievement.

☐ make sure you answer both parts of the question in your composition.

☐ organize your ideas so that the reader can clearly follow what you are saying.

☐ use only those details from the text that support the points you want to make.

☐ check your work for correct spelling, capitalization, punctuation, grammar, and sentences.

GO ON

⌐ **Common Core State Standards** ⌐

CCSS Writing 3.b. Use narrative techniques, such as dialogue, description, and pacing, to develop experiences and events or show the responses of characters to situations. (Also **CCSS Language 1., CCSS Language 3.**)

_____

_____

_____

_____

_____

_____

_____

_____

_____

_____

_____

_____

_____

_____

_____

_____

_____

_____

_____

_____

_____

VOCABULARY

Directions

Find the word or words with the same meaning as the underlined word. Circle the letter next to the answer.

1 Her <u>behavior</u> is odd.

    A benefactor

    (B) way of acting

    C pronunciation

    D way of dressing

2 This place is <u>sacred</u>.

    (F) holy

    G impressive

    H damaged

    J worthless

3 He was <u>astonished</u>.

    (A) surprised

    B worried

    C satisfied

    D dismissed

4 Her <u>gratitude</u> was overwhelming.

    F responsibility

    G weariness

    H inspiration

    (J) thankfulness

5 We watched the <u>procession</u>.

    A people playing a game

    B audience cheering

    (C) group moving together

    D workers planting crops

6 The <u>distribution</u> of clothing was done quickly.

    F display

    G tearing up

    H inspection

    (J) giving out

7 I <u>recommend</u> the pie.

    A appreciate

    (B) heartily suggest

    C deserve

    D graciously offer

GO ON

Common Core State Standards

Questions 1–7: CCSS Language 5.c. Use the relationship between particular words (e.g., synonyms, antonyms, homographs) to better understand each of the words.

WORD ANALYSIS OPTIONAL SUBTEST

Directions

Find the word or words with the same meaning as the underlined word. Circle the letter next to the answer.

8 Sandra bought an <u>imitation</u> designer handbag at the flea market.

   F real

   (G) fake

   H an emergency

   J to echo

9 I knew you were kind because of your <u>association</u> with the Nice Club.

   (A) connection

   B knowledge

   C business

   D giving money

10 Our dog needed plenty of <u>persuasion</u> to get into the water.

   F one who believes

   G in an urgent manner

   (H) the act of convincing

   J to urge

11 She offered to help without <u>hesitation</u>.

   A being confused

   B running late

   C doubting

   (D) pausing

12 The <u>promotion</u> helped her career.

   (F) move to a higher rank

   G advanced motion

   H advertisement

   J elevated height

GO ON

> **Common Core State Standards**

Questions 8–12: CCSS Language 5.c. Use the relationship between particular words (e.g., synonyms, antonyms, homographs) to better understand each of the words.

COMPREHENSION

"Big Mose"

Once there was a fireman named Moses. He lived in New York during the early 1800s. He was a big man with red hair. People say that he was eight feet tall! He was so strong that he was called "Big Mose."

One night, there was a fire. The other firemen put on their gear. Big Mose was a few blocks away, so he jumped through the air and got there first.

The fire was spreading fast. He needed a lot of water to put it out. He looked at the Hudson River and got an idea. He started digging a tunnel underneath the river. His shovel was as big as a trolley car.

Big Mose worked through the night. He kept digging the tunnel until he was under the spot where the fire was still burning. He was tired, but he knew he had the strength to beat the fire.

The other firemen were about to give up hope. "Stand back!" Big Mose told them.

He ran to the far end of the tunnel underneath the river. He swung an ax over his head, trying to break through into the river above. At first, only a few drops of water leaked into the tunnel. Big Mose swung the ax again, as hard as he could. Millions of gallons of water spilled into the tunnel.

Big Mose jumped up. He watched the water drain out of the river and into his tunnel. Within a few minutes, the fire was out. The riverbed was almost dry.

He went back to the scene of the fire. His fellow firemen and the people of New York cheered for him. "Hooray for Mose!" they roared. "Hooray for Mose!"

The riverbed eventually filled with water again, but Big Mose's tunnel remained. Many years later, it became the first subway tunnel in New York City.

GO ON

Directions

Choose the item that best answers each question about the selection you just read. Circle the letter next to the answer.

13 What is the main problem that Big Mose faces in the story?

    A   how to swim across the Hudson River

    (B)   how to get more water to fight a fire

    C   how to get along with the other firemen

    D   how to get around in New York

14 How is Big Mose different from other firemen in New York?

    (F)   He's stronger and faster.

    G   He has red hair.

    H   He carries an ax.

    J   He lives on the other side of the Hudson River.

15 In paragraph 3, the shovel that Big Mose uses to fight the fire is compared to

    A   an ax.

    (B)   a trolley car.

    C   a fire engine.

    D   a riverbed.

16 What is the last step Big Mose takes to fight the fire?

    F   He runs through the tunnel.

    (G)   He swings his ax as hard as he can.

    H   He swims across the river.

    J   He cheers for the other firemen.

17 The tunnel that Big Mose dug was different from other tunnels because

    A   it was for subway trains.

    (B)   it was used to fight a fire.

    C   it goes under the river.

    D   it was very wide.

18 Both the firemen and the people of New York cheer for Big Mose

    F   after he digs a tunnel.

    G   after he drains the river.

    (H)   after he puts out the fire.

    J   after he works all night.

19 As a fireman in New York, Big Mose could best be compared to

    (A)   a knight defending his country.

    B   a treasure hunter seeking a vast fortune.

    C   an explorer on a quest in a foreign land.

    D   a prince seeking power over others.

20 Where would this passage most likely be found?

    F   in a newspaper

    G   in a collection of autobiographies

    H   in a news magazine

    (J)   in a collection of folk tales

GO ON

Common Core State Standards

Questions 13, 15–16, 18–20: CCSS Literature 1. Quote accurately from a text when explaining what the text says explicitly and when drawing inferences from the text. Questions 14, 17: CCSS Literature 3. Compare and contrast two or more characters, settings, or events in a story or drama, drawing on specific details in the text (e.g., how characters interact).

WRITTEN RESPONSE TO THE SELECTION

Look Back and Write Look back at the question on page 237. How does the story *The Ch'i-lin Purse* show that one good deed deserves another?

The information in the box below will help you remember what you should think about when you write your composition.

REMEMBER—YOU SHOULD

☐ explain how the story shows that one good deed deserves another.

☐ use details from the story to support your answer.

☐ summarize the events of the story in your composition.

☐ tell about the events in the order in which they occur, using time order words to show sequence.

☐ check your work for correct spelling, capitalization, punctuation, grammar, and sentences.

Common Core State Standards

CCSS Writing 2.b. Develop the topic with facts, definitions, concrete details, quotations, or other information and examples related to the topic. (Also **CCSS Literature 1., CCSS Writing 2., CCSS Writing 4., CCSS Writing 9., CCSS Language 1.**)

_____

_____

_____

_____

_____

_____

_____

_____

_____

_____

_____

_____

_____

_____

_____

_____

_____

_____

_____

VOCABULARY

Directions

Find the word or words with the same meaning as the underlined word. Circle the letter next to the answer.

1 The view from my window included a <u>mesa</u>.

A deep rock-lined canyon

B hill with a gentle slope

C flat-topped land formation

D mountain with a high peak

2 My sister is wearing a new <u>bracelet</u>.

F piece of jewelry

G pair of shoes

H short-sleeve sweater

J fancy blouse

3 I liked the red <u>bandana</u> with the white pattern.

A tablecloth

B handkerchief

C quilt

D pillowcase

4 I bought my mother a piece of <u>Navajo</u> pottery.

F made by a Native American of a certain tribe

G made by an Asian from a certain country

H made by an African of a certain nation

J made by a Pacific Islander of a certain island

5 Yi was <u>jostled</u> by Kaia at the concert.

A forcefully stopped

B accompanied

C yelled at

D bumped against

6 Shylock gave his wife a silver ring set with a <u>turquoise</u>.

F bright red gemstone

G greenish-blue gemstone

H multicolored gemstone

J black gemstone

7 The <u>hogan</u> was cosy and warm.

A type of food

B type of shelter

C type of clothing

D type of furniture

GO ON

Common Core State Standards

Questions 1–7: CCSS Language 5.c. Use the relationship between particular words (e.g., synonyms, antonyms, homographs) to better understand each of the words.

WORD ANALYSIS

Directions

For each sentence, choose the correct word that is related to the underlined word. Circle the letter next to the answer.

8 The <u>plaza</u> was a delightful place to sit in the <u>sunshine</u>.

(F) town square
G living room
H playground
J park

9 Hervé gave the <u>burro</u> a lump of sugar.

A goat
B lamb
(C) donkey
D horse

10 The <u>adobe</u> walls kept the house cool in the summer.

F stone held together with mortar
(G) brick made from mud baked in the sun
H thatch made of dried hay
J logs plastered over on the inside

11 I saw a <u>llama</u> in the mountains.

(A) animal that looks like a camel
B bird that looks like a swan
C fish that looks like a shark
D insect that looks like a dragonfly

12 <u>Salsa</u> always makes me feel happy.

F type of seafood
(G) type of music
H type of dessert
J type of story

COMPREHENSION

El Niño: Changing the Weather

El Niño is a change in how warm the ocean is. It happens when warm water from the Pacific moves eastward. No one knows why this happens.

It takes place every four or five years and lasts for about a year. No two are the same. It can change the weather in many places at once. The United States is one of those places.

El Niño means "The Christ Child" in Spanish. This is a very appropriate name for the change in weather. It was named for the time when it is most powerful. This is often around Christmas. The warm water kills the food that most fish eat. This makes fishing hard. Many people fish for a living in South America.

GO ON

Common Core State Standards

Questions 8–12: CCSS Language 5.c. Use the relationship between particular words (e.g., synonyms, antonyms, homographs) to better understand each of the words.

During El Niño, places that often get a lot of rain become very dry. These include rainforests. They can have droughts and fires. Places that don't get much rain often have flooding. These include deserts.

In Africa, India, Australia, and Mexico, drought can cause many problems. Farmers cannot harvest their crops. This often leads to food shortages and even famine.

In the United States, it affects how much rain and snow falls during the winter. The Pacific Northwest usually has a drier-than-normal winter. States along the Gulf of Mexico are sometimes wetter than normal.

The Great Plains and upper Midwest tend to be warmer. This means fewer snowstorms. One unfortunate result is that people cannot ski. But on the East Coast, there are often more winter storms.

Not everything about El Niño is bad. Fewer hurricanes form in the Atlantic Ocean in the summer. The weather conditions are not right for them. Florida and North Carolina often get powerful hurricanes, but El Niño helps prevent them.

When El Niño ends, it is often followed by La Niña. This is another change in the ocean's water. Cold water from the Pacific flows east. It takes the place of warm water.

In the U.S., the weather during La Niña is often the opposite of El Niño. This means wet weather in the Pacific Northwest, and dry weather in the South. People do not enjoy the weather during La Niña.

Directions
Choose the item that best answers each question about the selection you just read. Circle the letter next to the answer.

13 In paragraph 3, the author's purpose is to

A describe the kind of weather Americans experience during El Niño.

B list the good effects El Niño has on some parts of the country.

(C) explain where El Niño got its name.

D show how El Niño differs from La Niña.

14 Why does the author include the information in the first paragraph?

(F) To define the topic for readers

G To show why the topic is important

H To grab readers' interest

J To explain why he is an expert on the topic

GO ON

Common Core State Standards

Questions 13–14: CCSS Informational Text 8. Explain how an author uses reasons and evidence to support particular points in a text, identifying which reasons and evidence support which point(s).

15 Which statement most accurately summarizes the effects of El Niño?

(A) El Niño causes weather changes throughout the world.

B El Niño hurts fishing for four to five years in South America.

C El Niño creates more rain and snow in the United States.

D El Niño helps farmers in Africa.

16 How is El Niño different from La Niña?

F El Niño causes fires; La Niña causes droughts.

G El Niño involves cold water; La Niña involves warm water.

H El Niño causes hurricanes; La Niña causes floods.

(J) El Niño involves warm water; La Niña involves cold water.

17 Which word makes the second sentence of paragraph 3 a statement of opinion?

A name

(B) appropriate

C change

D weather

18 In paragraphs 4 and 5, the author's main purpose is to

F describe what happens when La Niña occurs.

G explain how people can prevent El Niño.

H help readers understand why El Niño happens.

(J) describe the ill effects of El Niño in various places.

19 What was the author's main purpose in writing this passage?

(A) to inform the reader about the effects of El Niño

B to persuade the reader to do something about climate change

C to entertain the reader with a suspenseful true story

D to explain to the reader why El Niño happens

20 What was the author's main purpose in writing paragraphs 9 and 10?

F to explain why people don't like it when El Niño happens

G to describe the positive effects of La Niña

H to explain why people like it when El Niño happens

(J) to describe the negative effects of La Niña

GO ON

5   Copyright © Pearson Education, Inc., or its affiliates. All Rights Reserved.

⌐ **Common Core State Standards** ⌐

Questions 15, 17: CCSS Informational Text 1. Quote accurately from a text when explaining what the text says explicitly and when drawing inferences from the text. **Question 16: CCSS Informational Text 3.** Explain the relationships or interactions between two or more individuals, events, ideas, or concepts in a historical, scientific, or technical text based on specific information in the text. **Questions 18–20: CCSS Informational Text 8.** Explain how an author uses reasons and evidence to support particular points in a text, identifying which reasons and evidence support which point(s).

WRITTEN RESPONSE TO THE SELECTION

> **Look Back and Write** Look back at the last page of the story. How does the grandmother's trade of the saddle for a rug that she will make *in the future* add to Tony's good deed?

The information in the box below will help you remember what you should think about when you write your composition.

REMEMBER—YOU SHOULD

☐ explain why the grandmother's trade of the saddle for a rug that she will make in the future adds to Tony's good deed.

☐ make sure that each sentence you write helps the reader understand your composition.

☐ organize your thoughts to make your writing clear and logical for the reader.

☐ use details from the story to support your answer.

☐ check your work for correct spelling, capitalization, punctuation, grammar, and sentences.

⎫ **Common Core State Standards** ⎧

CCSS Writing 3.b. Use narrative techniques, such as dialogue, description, and pacing, to develop experiences and events or show the responses of characters to situations. (Also **CCSS Literature 2., CCSS Writing 3., CCSS Writing 4., CCSS Writing 5.**)

VOCABULARY

Directions

Find the word or words with the same meaning as the underlined word. Circle the letter next to the answer.

1 His surroundings were <u>somber</u>.

   A unfamiliar

   Ⓑ gloomy

   C uncomfortable

   D decaying

2 The <u>steed</u> walked across the field.

   Ⓕ high-spirited horse

   G riderless horse

   H unsaddled horse

   J bad-tempered horse

3 His <u>fate</u> has been determined.

   A assignment

   B advancement

   Ⓒ destiny

   D payment

4 The bug was <u>magnified</u> under the lens.

   F digging faster

   G resting quietly

   H caught suddenly

   Ⓙ made to look larger

5 We saw a <u>glimmer</u> in the distance.

   Ⓐ dim light

   B flowing creek

   C foggy valley

   D frightening sight

6 The captain of the ship was <u>fearless</u>.

   F fortunate

   G competitive

   Ⓗ bold

   J dedicated

7 The smell of smoke <u>lingers</u>.

   A advances

   Ⓑ stays

   C ascends

   D vanishes

GO ON

Common Core State Standards

Questions 1–7: CCSS Language 5.c. Use the relationship between particular words (e.g., synonyms, antonyms, homographs) to better understand each of the words.

WORD ANALYSIS

Directions

Find the word in the same word family as the underlined word. Circle the letter next to the answer.

8 We have nothing to <u>fear</u> about camping in the woods.

F scared

G leap

(H) near

D unafraid

9 He bought the latest fishing <u>gear</u> for his vacation.

A groan

(B) clear

C hat

D supply

10 Do you know what <u>year</u> it is?

F stare

G time

H jeer

(J) dear

11 She didn't <u>hear</u> the train whistle.

A listen

(B) spear

C pearl

D great

12 The sky was very <u>clear</u> this morning.

F weight

G chair

(H) rear

J care

COMPREHENSION

The Abenaki

The Abenaki are a group of Native Americans. They lived in what is now New England and Canada when the Europeans first arrived. They lived in villages or small towns.

The kind of house built by the Abenaki was called a wigwam. It was shaped like a cone. A wigwam was covered in bark from trees. Many Abenaki caught fish for food. Spring and fall were important times to fish. During these seasons, the rivers were full of fish. Other Abenaki were hunters who spent their days in the forest. Some were farmers who harvested crops, such as corn.

GO ON

Common Core State Standards

Questions 8–12: CCSS Foundational Skills 3.a. Use combined knowledge of all letter-sound correspondences, syllabication patterns, and morphology (e.g., roots and affixes) to read accurately unfamiliar multisyllabic words in context and out of context.

The Abenaki first came into contact with European explorers in the 1500s. The Abenaki traded things, such as fur, with these explorers. During the 1600s, the number of Europeans living on Abenaki land grew. The Europeans caused problems for the Abenaki. Diseases from Europe killed many of the Abenaki by the middle of the 1700s. Before contact with Europeans, there may have been as many as forty thousand Abenaki. Today, there are about twelve thousand in the United States and Canada.

By the late 1600s, British settlers had begun to surround Abenaki land. The Abenaki found themselves in battles with the British. Sometimes they won these battles. Sometimes they lost. At times they would leave their homes when the British came near. They would come back when the danger had passed. Others left their homes for good.

In the early 1900s, many Abenaki saw their way of life change. They lost much of their land. Factories began polluting the rivers where they fished.

Today, many Abenaki still live in New England and Quebec. They have been able to buy back some of the land they lost. They are fighting for the right to fish in local rivers. They hope to protect their way of life.

Directions

Choose the item that best answers each question about the selection you just read. Circle the letter next to the answer.

13 Why did the author write this article?

  A to tell true stories about the Abenaki's wars with Europeans

  Ⓑ to tell how the Abenaki have changed since encountering Europeans

  C to persuade the reader to live like the Abenaki in the 1500s

  D to tell how Europeans traded with the Abenaki for fur

14 This passage is mostly about

  F challenges facing the Abenaki today.

  G changes to the Abenaki way of life in the 1800s.

  Ⓗ the history of the Abenaki.

  J details about traditional Abenaki life.

GO ON

Common Core State Standards

Question 13: CCSS Informational Text 8. Explain how an author uses reasons and evidence to support particular points in a text, identifying which reasons and evidence support which point(s). **Question 14: CCSS Informational Text 2.** Determine two or more main ideas of a text and explain how they are supported by key details; summarize the text.

15 The author included the information in paragraph 2

   A to describe the effects of history on today's Abenaki population.

   B to grab the reader's attention with an exciting tale.

   C to describe the conflicts between Europeans and Native Americans.

   (D) to share details about the traditional life of the Abenaki.

16 Why had many Abenaki died by the middle of the 1700s?

   F They ran out of food.

   (G) Diseases from Europe killed them.

   H They were forced to leave their homes and could not survive the winters.

   J They were killed in battles.

17 What does the author think about conflicts between the Abenaki and the Europeans?

   (A) She is sympathetic to the Abenaki.

   B She is sympathetic to the Europeans.

   C She is equally sympathetic to both sides.

   D She thinks both sides were wrong to fight.

18 What generalization can you make about the Abenaki?

   (F) They believe it is important to hold on to their way of life.

   G They did not care about the problems caused by the Europeans.

   H They are very cautious when meeting strangers.

   J They were no match for the British army.

19 The author includes the information in paragraph 6 in order to

   A explain why the Abenaki were not successful against the Europeans.

   B describe the conflicts between the Abenaki and the Europeans.

   (C) inform interested readers of the Abenaki's current status.

   D persuade readers that the Abenaki are a heroic people.

20 What is the author's main purpose in paragraphs 3 and 4?

   F to describe the everyday lives of the Abenaki

   (G) to show how European migration to North America affected the Abenaki

   H to explain why the Europeans and Abenaki could not live peacefully together

   J to explain why the Abenaki want to buy back their traditional lands

GO ON

⌐ **Common Core State Standards** ⌐

Questions 15, 17, 19–20: CCSS Informational Text 8. Explain how an author uses reasons and evidence to support particular points in a text, identifying which reasons and evidence support which point(s). **Question 16: CCSS Informational Text 3.** Explain the relationships or interactions between two or more individuals, events, ideas, or concepts in a historical, scientific, or technical text based on specific information in the text. **Question 18: CCSS Informational Text 1.** Quote accurately from a text when explaining what the text says explicitly and when drawing inferences from the text.

WRITTEN RESPONSE TO THE SELECTION

Look Back and Write Look back at pages 300–305. How did Paul Revere feel before and during his ride? Use evidence from the text to support your answer.

The information in the box below will help you remember what you should think about when you write your composition.

REMEMBER—YOU SHOULD

☐   explain how Paul Revere felt before and during his ride.

☐   draw conclusions about Revere's feelings based on details in the poem.

☐   use details from the poem to support your answer.

☐   communicate your thoughts and ideas about Revere as clearly as possible so that the reader understands what you are saying.

☐   check your work for correct spelling, capitalization, punctuation, grammar, and sentences.

GO ON

Common Core State Standards

CCSS Writing 3.b. Use narrative techniques, such as dialogue, description, and pacing, to develop experiences and events or show the responses of characters to situations. (Also **CCSS Literature 1., CCSS Language 1., CCSS Language 3., CCSS Writing 3.a., CCSS Writing 3.d.**)

VOCABULARY

Directions
Find the word or words with the same meaning as the underlined word. Circle the letter next to the answer.

1 She looks <u>fabulous</u> in her new dress.

  A tired

  B scared

  Ⓒ extraordinary

  D unattractive

2 He wants to continue <u>browsing</u> in the library.

  F studying

  Ⓖ casually looking

  H napping

  J making noise

3 They will be <u>inspecting</u> the factory tomorrow.

  Ⓐ carefully looking at

  B thoroughly cleaning

  C changing the location of

  D building

4 The town has started a <u>project</u> to widen Main Street.

  F application

  G idea

  H permit

  Ⓙ plan

5 An audience usually <u>applauds</u> after a great performance.

  A remains quiet

  Ⓑ claps

  C yells

  D leaves

GO ON

Common Core State Standards

Questions 1–5: CCSS Language 5.c. Use the relationship between particular words (e.g., synonyms, antonyms, homographs) to better understand each of the words.

WORD ANALYSIS

Directions

Find the word or words with the same meaning as the underlined word. Circle the letter next to the answer.

6 My teacher is very <u>special</u>.

    F good

    G proper

    (H) unusual

    J ordinary

7 Her new car was <u>shiny</u>.

    (A) sparkling

    B dull

    C blinding

    D clean

8 Tomorrow is supposed to be a <u>beautiful</u> day.

    F cloudy

    (G) gorgeous

    H adequate

    J awful

9 The light in this room is so <u>dim</u> that I can't read.

    A brilliant

    B murky

    C dull

    (D) faint

10 He was <u>unaware</u> that he was late for class.

    F conscious

    (G) ignorant

    H ignored

    J innocent

11 The apple crisp is <u>delicious</u>.

    A tasteless

    B sweet

    (C) tasty

    D rich

12 The wind blew <u>fiercely</u> during the storm.

    (F) strongly

    G quickly

    H weakly

    J gently

GO ON

Common Core State Standards

Questions 6–12: CCSS Language 5.c. Use the relationship between particular words (e.g., synonyms, antonyms, homographs) to better understand each of the words.

COMPREHENSION

Cast Your Vote

In 1789, Philadelphia was the largest and most important city in a brand-new nation. The thirteen colonies of Great Britain had just won a war. They had become a new country called the United States of America.

Every country needs a government. Leaders from all thirteen states met in Philadelphia to create one. This group, called the Congress, wrote a Constitution. It set forth the rules for the new government of the United States.

The United States is a republic. This means that the people vote for leaders who will represent them. Leaders speak up for your views on the issues and work to pass the laws you support. In 1789, very few countries allowed their citizens to vote. Even in the United States, only certain citizens could vote. The Constitution said that white men could vote if they were at least 21 years old. This was less than thirty percent of all Americans.

Over time, the laws changed. Americans fought a Civil War to free African American slaves. Soon after the war, the government passed new laws. African American men began voting in 1868.

Women had fought for the right to vote all along. Abigail Adams, later the First Lady of the country, urged her husband John to "remember the ladies" in the new code of laws. But Congress did not agree with this view. American women marched in parades and held protests in an effort to change the law. In 1920, Congress finally changed the Constitution so that women could vote.

In 1924, Congress passed a law stating that American Indians were full citizens. This meant that they had the right to vote. Indians had been in North America much longer than any other group of people. However, they were among the last to be allowed to vote.

Many white people in the South did not want African Americans to vote. They charged a tax for voting, called a poll tax. Many African Americans were too poor to pay the poll tax, so they did not vote. In 1964, Congress declared that poll taxes were illegal. Thousands more African Americans could vote.

America was at war with Vietnam during the 1960s. Many teenagers protested against the war. Teenage boys were especially angry, because they could be forced to serve in the army. They argued that if they were old enough to be sent into battle, they were old enough to vote for the leaders who sent them. In 1971, the government lowered the voting age to 18. They agreed it was only fair that soldiers in the army should be able to vote.

GO ON

Directions

Choose the item that best answers each question about the selection you just read. Circle the letter next to the answer.

13 Which group could vote before any of the others?

   A American Indians age 21 and over

   B teenagers

   (C) white men age 21 and over

   D women age 21 and over

14 When did the government outlaw the poll tax?

   F 1789

   G 1920

   (H) 1964

   J 1971

15 The last group of people to be given the vote was

   (A) teenagers.

   B American Indians.

   C women.

   D men.

16 What did the leaders do after they arrived in Philadelphia in 1789?

   F fought a war

   G remembered the ladies

   H changed the laws

   (J) wrote a Constitution

17 In 1971, leaders expressed the opinion that teenagers should

   A not serve in the army.

   B protest the Vietnam War.

   C run for office.

   (D) be allowed to vote.

18 The author wrote this article in order to

   F entertain the reader with exciting true stories.

   (G) recount the history of voting in the United States.

   H persuade the reader to register to vote.

   J persuade the reader to change the laws.

19 Which law was passed first?

   A the law giving Indians the right to vote

   B the law outlawing the poll tax

   (C) the law giving women the right to vote

   D the law giving teenagers the right to vote

20 From the information in paragraph 7, you can conclude that

   (F) only Southern states charged a poll tax.

   G African Americans were wealthier than white people.

   H Southern states did not charge a poll tax.

   J Northern states charged a poll tax.

GO ON

Common Core State Standards

Questions 13–16, 19: CCSS Informational Text 1. Quote accurately from a text when explaining what the text says explicitly and when drawing inferences from the text. **Question 18: CCSS Informational Text 2.** Determine two or more main ideas of a text and explain how they are supported by key details; summarize the text. **Questions 17, 20: CCSS Informational Text 3.** Explain the relationships or interactions between two or more individuals, events, ideas, or concepts in a historical, scientific, or technical text based on specific information in the text.

WRITTEN RESPONSE TO THE SELECTION

> **Look Back and Write** Look through the play. What goals do Lily and Carlos have for inventing their machine other than winning the prize at the science fair? Are these the goals you would have if you invented such a machine? Provide evidence to support your answer.

The information in the box below will help you remember what you should think about when you write your composition.

REMEMBER—YOU SHOULD

☐ tell Lily and Carlos's goals for inventing their machine and explain if these would be your goals if you invented such a machine.

☐ answer each part of the question in your composition.

☐ use details from the play to support your answer.

☐ provide a clear statement of your opinion in your answer to the second part of the question with reasons that support your opinion.

☐ check your work for correct spelling, capitalization, punctuation, grammar, and sentences.

GO ON

Common Core State Standards

CCSS Writing 1. Write opinion pieces on topics or texts, supporting a point of view with reasons and information. (Also **CCSS Writing 3.a., CCSS Writing 3.b., CCSS Writing 3.c., CCSS Language 1.**)

_____

_____

_____

_____

_____

_____

_____

_____

_____

_____

_____

_____

_____

_____

_____

_____

_____

_____

_____

_____

_____

_____

VOCABULARY

Directions

Find the word or words with the same meaning as the underlined word. Circle the letter next to the answer.

1 The <u>architect</u> was a talented woman.

(A) building designer

B safety inspector

C worldly philosopher

D medical technician

2 She <u>fashioned</u> a hat for herself.

F purchased

G refused

H selected

(J) made

3 The tray was made from <u>bronze</u>.

A metal used to make cannons

B metal made of copper and silver

(C) metal made of copper and tin

D flexible metal

4 The man was <u>depressed</u>.

(F) sad

G tense

H satisfied

J compassionate

5 There is a fountain in the <u>midst</u> of the garden.

(A) center

B corner

C extension

D entry

6 Her <u>rival</u> did not play fair.

F one who plays in a tournament

(G) one who competes against another

H one who practices frequently

J one who teaches sports

7 The girl <u>achieved</u> many things.

A earned

B provided

(C) accomplished

D performed

GO ON

Common Core State Standards

Questions 1–7: CCSS Language 5.c. Use the relationship between particular words (e.g., synonyms, antonyms, homographs) to better understand each of the words.

WORD ANALYSIS

Directions
Choose the word that answers each question. Circle the letter next to the answer.

8 That movie came out on <u>video</u> in 1985.

What does the word *video* mean?

F   a device that lets you read the movie

G   a device that lets you hear the movie

(H)   a device that lets you see the movie

J   a device that lets you act out the movie

9 The mountaintop was <u>visible</u> through the clouds.

The word *visible* contains the Latin root *vis*, meaning

(A)   "to see."

B   "to climb."

C   "to disappear."

D   "to rise."

10 The <u>spectators</u> became angry after the game was delayed.

The word *spectators* contains the Latin root *spect*, meaning

F   "to buy."

G   "to play."

H   "to sit."

(J)   "to observe."

11 I want to study <u>philosophy</u> when I go to college.

The word *philosophy* contains the Greek root *philo*, meaning

A   "study."

B   "wisdom."

C   "teach."

(D)   "love."

12 Which of the following words means "to look at something closely"?

F   spectacle

(G)   inspect

H   expect

D   respect

GO ON

⌐ **Common Core State Standards** ⌐

Questions 8–12: CCSS Language 4.b. Use common, grade-appropriate Greek and Latin affixes and roots as clues to the meaning of a word (e.g., photograph, photosynthesis).

COMPREHENSION

The Amazing Nicola Tesla

You have probably heard of Thomas Edison and Alexander Graham Bell—but do you know the name Nicola Tesla? Edison invented the electric light, the phonograph, and motion pictures, among other things. Bell invented the telephone. Nicola Tesla was also a genius of science. Tesla invented most of the equipment for the kind of electric power we use today, and he was a pioneer in radio. But his achievements were overshadowed by people who were better at raising money for their experiments.

Nicola Tesla was born in 1856 in a part of Austria-Hungary that is now Serbia. He went to school in Austria. As a young man, he worked with power companies in many European cities. Tesla came to the United States in 1884 and got a job with Thomas Edison. Their partnership did not last very long. Edison thought that Tesla was brilliant, but he didn't think Tesla's ideas were practical.

Tesla then went to work for George Westinghouse, who was building an electric-power company. During this time, Tesla created most of the equipment we use today to power our homes, offices, and factories. One of his most important inventions was the Tesla coil, a device that boosts power. Later, the Tesla coil would be used for radio and television. Tesla helped Westinghouse bring electric power to the 1893 World's Fair in Chicago. This was the first time many Americans witnessed the beauty of electric lights.

One day in 1898, Tesla put on an amazing show in Madison Square Garden in New York City. On the stage was an artificial pond with a toy boat. Sitting up in the stands with the spectators, Tesla made the boat move with a remote control. People at that time could not imagine remote control, and they thought Tesla was using his own brain power to move the boat. His invention was the beginning of what we call *robotics* today.

About the same time, Tesla was working long hours in his lab on radio. He believed he could prove that radio waves could send information over long distances. However, an Italian inventor named Marconi beat Tesla. Marconi received money from rich Europeans to help him with his research. He got the credit—and the money—for inventing radio. Tesla was upset. If he had received financial support for his project, he might well have been recognized as the inventor of radio.

Tesla died in 1943. He has come to be recognized as one of the greatest inventors of modern times.

GO ON

Directions

Choose the item that best answers each question about the selection you just read. Circle the letter next to the answer.

13 Based on the passage, which achievement *cannot* be claimed for Nicola Tesla?

    A invention of remote control

    B development of equipment for power generation and transmission

    (C) invention of the first practical, indoor electric light

    D contributions to the development of radio and television

14 Which statement about Marconi is true?

    F He introduced the world to electric lights.

    G He did not work well with other Europeans.

    H He lost interest in radio before he achieved any successes with it.

    (J) He was successful at getting financial backing for his scientific work.

15 What do you think George Westinghouse might say about Nicola Tesla?

    A "Nice guy, but not very bright or inventive."

    B "I had to fire him because he didn't perform."

    (C) "He surpassed my expectations."

    D "He messed up the Chicago World's Fair."

16 Which statement expresses an opinion?

    F The electric lights at the World's Fair were beautiful.

    (G) Marconi received the credit for inventing radio.

    H Tesla's partnership with Edison did not last long.

    J Tesla invented a device that boosted power.

17 Which dates indicate Tesla's lifespan?

    (A) 1856–1943

    B 1884–1943

    C 1893–1898

    D 1856–1898

18 Radio and television depend on which of Tesla's inventions?

    F Tesla generator

    (G) Tesla coil

    H Tesla fuel pump

    J Tesla tube

19 Tesla's contributions to radio are so important that

    A Marconi needed his help to finish the job.

    B rich Europeans deserted Marconi and backed Tesla instead.

    C Thomas Edison asked him back to work.

    (D) he might have been known as the inventor of radio if he had gotten financial backing.

20 Which statement best expresses the main idea of this reading selection?

    F Edison had good reasons to think Tesla's ideas were impractical.

    (G) Tesla was one of the greatest modern inventors, though he was overlooked.

    H All brilliant thinkers and innovators are alike.

    J Humankind tamed electric power once and for all in the late 1800s.

GO ON

Common Core State Standards

Questions 13, 15, 18–20: CCSS Informational Text 2. Determine two or more main ideas of a text and explain how they are supported by key details; summarize the text. **Questions 14, 16, 17: CCSS Informational Text 1.** Quote accurately from a text when explaining what the text says explicitly and when drawing inferences from the text.

WRITTEN RESPONSE TO THE SELECTION

> **Look Back and Write** Look back at pages 376–377. Did Leonardo da Vinci's greatest dream ever come true? Provide evidence to support your answer.

The information in the box below will help you remember what you should think about when you write your composition.

REMEMBER—YOU SHOULD

- ☐ tell if Leonardo da Vinci's greatest dream ever came true.

- ☐ identify for readers da Vinci's greatest dream.

- ☐ use details from the text as evidence to support your answer.

- ☐ make sure that each sentence you write helps the reader understand your composition.

- ☐ check your work for correct spelling, capitalization, punctuation, grammar, and sentences.

GO ON

/ **Common Core State Standards** \

CCSS Writing 1.a. Introduce a topic or text clearly, state an opinion, and create an organizational structure in which ideas are logically grouped to support the writer's purpose. (Also **CCSS Writing 5., CCSS Language 1.**)

VOCABULARY

Directions

Find the word or words with the same meaning as the underlined word. Circle the letter next to the answer.

1 The work I did was in **proportion** to the pay I received.

   A correct installation among parts

   B realistic exhibition of color

   C correct relationship between items

   D realistic demonstration of movement

2 The builder made the **foundations** first.

   F covered ramps

   G enclosed passageways

   H sturdy, outer frames

   J supporting base structures

3 She entered the **workshop**.

   A room where items are sold

   B room where workers hold meetings

   C room where items are made

   D room where workers are trained

4 The memorial was **erected** last year.

   F built

   G expanded

   H designed

   J presented

5 The artist used a **mold**.

   A metal tool

   B hollow form

   C stretched canvas

   D special paintbrush

6 We **tidied** the classroom.

   F cleaned and organized

   G enlarged and decorated

   H maintained and exhibited

   J inspected and rebuilt

7 It was an **occasion** that everyone enjoyed.

   A familiar occurrence

   B skilled performance

   C planned meeting

   D special event

GO ON

Common Core State Standards

Questions 1–7: CCSS Language 5.c. Use the relationship between particular words (e.g., synonyms, antonyms, homographs) to better understand each of the words.

WORD ANALYSIS

Directions
Choose the correct spelling of the word that completes the blank. Circle the letter next to the word that fills the bank.

8 Many people worry about the problem of _____.

(F) pollution
G pollusion
H polluxion
J pollucian

9 At the graduation ceremony, the graduates marched in _____.

A precession
(B) procession
C prosession
D presession

10 I would like a larger _____ of the pizza, please.

F porshun
G porsion
H porshin
(J) portion

11 The radio reporter described a four-car _____ on the highway.

A collition
(B) collision
C collishun
D collisian

12 The television isn't working because a _____ is loose.

(F) connection
G connecshun
H connectshun
J connectsion

COMPREHENSION

Who Was William Shakespeare?

William Shakespeare, who lived 400 years ago in England, wrote more than 30 plays and more than 150 poems. Shakespeare's words have been repeated more than those of any other English-language author. Do you know the names Romeo and Juliet? They are characters in a play by Shakespeare about young people in love. Did you ever hear anyone say, "Parting is such sweet sorrow"? Shakespeare penned those words for Juliet to speak to Romeo.

GO ON

Common Core State Standards

Questions 8–12: CCSS Language 2.e. Spell grade-appropriate words correctly, consulting references as needed.

William Shakespeare was born in the small town of Stratford-on-Avon, England, in 1564. When he grew up he married Anne Hathaway, and they had three children. Later, Shakespeare went to London, the largest and most exciting city in England. He joined a theater company so he could write and act in plays. Shakespeare was so successful that he was able to purchase one of the biggest houses in Stratford-on-Avon in 1597.

Powerful and important people such as aristocrats, kings, and queens enjoyed Shakespeare's plays. England's ruler, Queen Elizabeth I, was one of his fans. King James I, who took the throne when Elizabeth died, also lavished praise on Shakespeare.

When Shakespeare retired from the theater business, he moved back to his grand house in Stratford-on-Avon, where he died in 1616.

Shakespeare lived in an age long before newspapers, radio news broadcasts, TV talk shows, movies, or cell phones. There are long periods in his life about which we know nothing. Also, the spelling of his name and his signature are not always the same on papers from his time. After the writer's death, some people did not believe the plays and poems of "Shakespeare" were really written by the man of that name. Today, people still argue about this question.

Some people point out that Shakespeare was a small-town boy who never went to college or traveled very far. They do not think that William Shakespeare had enough knowledge to have written the great plays and poems. They think that a wealthier, better-educated person must have been the real "Shakespeare."

Derek Jacobi, a famous English actor, has said that there is reason to wonder who Shakespeare really was. He is in good company. The famous American writer Mark Twain believed that the real writer of Shakespeare's plays was some person who has been lost to history. The English writer Charles Dickens said that the life of Shakespeare was "a fine mystery." Orson Welles, a famous American actor and director, said he thought the Earl of Oxford, who was a powerful nobleman, actually wrote the works.

On the other hand, many people still believe that William Shakespeare of Stratford-on-Avon wrote the plays that bear his name. They say that a good imagination is more important to a successful writer than education or travel or wealth.

Perhaps it doesn't matter whether we know who the true Shakespeare was. We can still enjoy his plays and poems—whoever he was.

GO ON

Directions

Choose the item that best answers each question about the reading selection you just read. Circle the letter next to the answer.

13 Which phrase does *not* state a fact about William Shakespeare?

  A   He was born in 1564.

  Ⓑ   He was a better writer than actor.

  C   He died in 1616.

  D   He wrote over 150 poems.

14 Which statement can be proved?

  F   Shakespeare was the most popular person in Stratford-on-Avon.

  G   In Shakespeare's time, Stratford-on-Avon was a boring place to live.

  Ⓗ   "Parting is such sweet sorrow" is a line from the play *Romeo and Juliet*.

  J   Queen Elizabeth I was a better ruler than King James I.

15 Which of the following graphic features would add the most to this selection?

  Ⓐ   a table listing the major works of Shakespeare

  B   a time line of Mark Twain's life

  C   a diagram of a Shakespearean theater

  D   a photograph of Derek Jacobi

16 Which statement expresses an opinion?

  F   Shakespeare was a writer.

  G   Shakespeare lived in London for a time.

  H   Shakespeare married Anne Hathaway.

  Ⓙ   Shakespeare was a great writer.

17 Which phrase explains why Shakespeare joined a theater company?

  A   so he could be friends with actors

  B   so he could visit Queen Elizabeth I

  C   so he could live in London

  Ⓓ   so he could write and act in plays

18 Which person does not express an opinion about Shakespeare?

  Ⓕ   the Earl of Oxford

  G   Derek Jacobi

  H   Mark Twain

  J   Orson Welles

19 When Dickens calls Shakespeare "a fine mystery," he is expressing his opinion that

  A   the plays and poems written by Shakespeare are hard to understand.

  B   Shakespeare was the best mystery writer ever.

  Ⓒ   there are a lot of unanswered questions about Shakespeare's life.

  D   writers never reveal very much about themselves.

20 What is the main idea of this passage?

  F   Kings, queens, and other powerful people of England used to enjoy the theater.

  Ⓖ   We do not know for sure who actually wrote under the name "Shakespeare."

  H   Stratford-on-Avon, England, is one of the most famous places in the world.

  J   *Romeo and Juliet* is everyone's favorite Shakespearean play.

GO ON

╭ **Common Core State Standards** ╮

Questions 13–19: CCSS Informational Text 1. Quote accurately from a text when explaining what the text says explicitly and when drawing inferences from the text. **Question 20: CCSS Informational Text 2.** Determine two or more main ideas of a text and explain how they are supported by key details; summarize the text.

WRITTEN RESPONSE TO THE SELECTION

Look Back and Write Look back at the story. Describe the way Waterhouse Hawkins introduced the world to a new kind of creature. Provide evidence from the text to support your answer.

The information in the box below will help you remember what you should think about when you write your composition.

REMEMBER—YOU SHOULD

☐ describe the way Waterhouse Hawkins introduced the world to a new kind of creature.

☐ summarize events and choose only the most important details as evidence.

☐ use time-order words to indicate the sequence of events.

☐ use descriptive words to explain what Waterhouse Hawkins did.

☐ check your work for correct spelling, capitalization, punctuation, grammar, and sentences.

⟩ **Common Core State Standards** ⟩

CCSS Writing 2. Write informative/explanatory texts to examine a topic and convey ideas and information clearly.
(Also **CCSS Writing 4.**, **CCSS Writing 5.**)

VOCABULARY

Directions

Find the word or words with the same meaning as the underlined word. Circle the letter next to the answer.

1 We learn about <u>slavery</u> in social studies.

  A the protection of private property
  Ⓑ the practice of owning another person
  C the selling of goods and services
  D the ways that laws are passed

2 Police <u>released</u> a picture of the man they were looking for.

  F displayed
  G threw out
  H approved
  Ⓙ made public

3 My sister is a <u>teenager</u>.

  Ⓐ someone between thirteen and nineteen years old
  B mature person
  C someone between one and ten years old
  D special person

4 He doesn't <u>appreciate</u> expensive clothes.

  F purchase
  G desire
  Ⓗ value
  J mend

5 My mother is in the <u>choir</u>.

  A gallery
  Ⓑ group of singers
  C courtyard
  D group of players

6 He is a <u>religious</u> man.

  F easily upset or angered
  G careless
  H innocent
  Ⓙ having a belief in one or more gods

7 Her cousin is a <u>barber</u>.

  A one who makes bread
  B one who invents things
  Ⓒ one who cuts hair
  D one who works in a garden

GO ON

| **Common Core State Standards** |

Questions 1–7: CCSS Language 5.c. Use the relationship between particular words (e.g., synonyms, antonyms, homographs) to better understand each of the words.

WORD ANALYSIS

Directions

Find the word or words with same meaning as the underlined word. Circle the letter next to the answer.

8 Did you ever meet a truly <u>famous</u> person?

F wicked

(G) known far and wide

H old

J good-looking

9 It is going to be a <u>glorious</u> summer!

A sizzling

(B) wonderful

C tragic

D miserable

10 I think you will enjoy this <u>humorous</u> story.

(F) funny

G scary

H very long

J true to life

11 What do you think about the <u>mysterious</u> disappearance of the main character?

A complicated

B gradual

(C) hard to explain

D loud and violent

12 Keep an eye out for <u>poisonous</u> snakes!

(F) deadly

G harmless

H inferior

J quiet, shy

> **Common Core State Standards**

Questions 8–12: CCSS Language 5.c. Use the relationship between particular words (e.g., synonyms, antonyms, homographs) to better understand each of the words.

COMPREHENSION

Good News About Biofuels

It is quite easy to ignore the fact that we use lots of energy every single day. Electricity powers devices in our homes, and natural gas or coal keeps us warm on cold days. Every time we ride in a car, we use up gas, which is made from oil.

We turn a key, flip a switch, or press an "on" button to get quick results—and that's the way we like it. It's not as simple as that, however. Behind the things we use and enjoy in our daily lives is a never-ending search for *fuel*, or material from which energy comes.

Some of our fuels may be running out. Fossil fuels, such as coal, oil, and natural gas, come from deep inside the Earth where they formed over millions of years. Coal, for example, formed when large amounts of dead trees and other plants were squeezed together for up to 300 million years! The problem is that we are using up coal, oil, and natural gas much faster than they can be formed inside the Earth.

More than half of our useful energy comes from fossil fuels, but they present another problem. Burning them for energy *emits* many kinds of pollution. Many scientists believe the pollution that is being released is trapping the sun's heat within our planet's atmosphere, and this is causing global warming.

One bright spot in this picture is the biofuels industry. Biofuels are made from crops that can be grown repeatedly and are therefore described as renewable. *Renewable* means "able to be produced again and again." Fossil fuels are not renewable.

A fuel called ethanol is made from corn, sugar cane, and other crops. Have you heard of E85? It is a special fuel made up mostly of ethanol and a little gasoline. Supporters of ethanol believe it may be the key to solving our energy crisis. On the other hand, some people say that food crops should not be used to produce ethanol because there are too many hungry people in the world.

Biodiesel is another source of renewable energy. It is made from canola oil or oils in plants such as soybeans. Biodiesel can be used in truck engines and other large engines that normally run on a type of fuel called diesel.

Ethanol, biodiesel, and other biofuels will probably not solve all of our energy problems, but to many people, they seem like a step in the right direction. Of course, we can also cut the amount of energy we use carelessly. So next time, think before you turn that key, flip that switch, or press that "on" button.

GO ON

Directions

Choose the item that best answers each question about the selection you just read. Circle the letter next to the answer.

13 Which fact contributes to the energy crisis we face?

  A Science has provided better and better ways to drill for oil.

  B There is a limitless supply of energy in sunlight.

  C People used to do work mainly by human power or animal power.

  (D) People expect to have limitless energy whenever they want.

14 Which statement best describes the process by which coal forms?

  (F) Dead plants are pressed together for thousands of years.

  G Tiny dead animals are pressed together for thousands of years.

  H The sun heats dead plants to high temperatures.

  J Rocks soak up oil and turn black.

15 Which sentence expresses an opinion?

  A Ethanol can be made from corn or sugar cane.

  (B) Food crops should not be used for ethanol because of world hunger.

  C Ethanol and biodiesel are two types of biofuels.

  D E85 is a mixture of ethanol and gasoline.

16 From which material is gasoline made?

  F wood

  (G) oil

  H corn

  J sugar cane

17 Which sentence describes a serious drawback of using fossil fuels?

  (A) They give off dangerous pollution in Earth's atmosphere.

  B They can be burned to produce energy.

  C They can be found in many parts of the world.

  D Our economy is set up to use fossil feuls for energy.

18 What is one big advantage of biofuels over fossil fuels?

  F Biofuels don't have an unpleasant odor.

  (G) Biofuels are renewable.

  H Biofuels are easy to move from place to place.

  J Biofuels last a long time when stored.

19 Which statement is a generalization?

  (A) We use lots of energy every single day.

  B Some of our fuels have run out.

  C Biodiesel is another form of renewable energy.

  D Think before you turn that key.

20 Which is the best statement of the main idea of this reading selection?

  F Ethanol is made from corn, sugar cane, or other similar crops.

  G Fossil fuels take millions of years to form inside the Earth.

  H We like having ample energy at our fingertips.

  (J) Biofuels may be an important part of the solution to our energy needs.

GO ON

Common Core State Standards

Questions 13, 15, 19: CCSS Informational Text 1. Quote accurately from a text when explaining what the text says explicitly and when drawing inferences from the text. **Questions 14, 16–18, 20: CCSS Informational Text 2.** Determine two or more main ideas of a text and explain how they are supported by key details; summarize the text.

WRITTEN RESPONSE TO THE SELECTION

> **Look Back and Write** Look back at the text. How did Mahalia Jackson use the blues in a new and different way? Provide evidence from the text to support your answer.

The information in the box below will help you remember what you should think about when you write your composition.

REMEMBER—YOU SHOULD

☐   explain how Mahalia Jackson used the blues in a new and different way.

☐   use details from the selection to support the points you make.

☐   explain the blues to the reader so that he or she understands how Mahalia Jackson used them in a different way.

☐   make your writing colorful and interesting for your reader.

☐   check your work for correct spelling, capitalization, punctuation, grammar, and sentences.

GO ON

Common Core State Standards

CCSS Writing 2.b. Develop the topic with facts, definitions, concrete details, quotations, or other information and examples related to the topic. (Also **CCSS Writing 2.d., CCSS Language 1.**)

VOCABULARY

*D*irections
Find the word or words with the same meaning as the underlined word. Circle the letter next to the answer.

1 The <u>explosions</u> made us nervous.

   A inspections

   (B) violent bursts

   C preparations

   D flashing lights

2 We saw a <u>miniature</u> pony.

   F sturdy

   G saddled

   H sleek

   (J) small

3 Dinosaurs were <u>prehistoric</u> animals.

   (A) relating to times before written history

   B told about throughout history

   C drawn by artists in historical books

   D found in several historical periods

4 He <u>reassembled</u> his model after it fell on the floor.

   F threw away

   (G) made whole again

   H repacked carefully

   J cleaned hurriedly

5 The <u>landscape</u> was covered with wildflowers.

   A mountain range

   B dense thicket

   (C) view of scenery on land

   D end of a peninsula

6 The photograph's <u>background</u> was dark.

   F what can be seen by an expert

   G what is seen near the corners of the frame

   (H) what is seen behind the subject

   J what is seen by looking closely

GO ON

Common Core State Standards

Questions 1–6: CCSS Language 5.c. Use the relationship between particular words (e.g., synonyms, antonyms, homographs) to better understand each of the words.

WORD ANALYSIS OPTIONAL SUBTEST

Directions
Find the compound word in each sentence. Circle the letter next to the answer.

7 The heavy humidity and growing darkness warned of a coming downpour.

   A darkness

   (B) downpour

   C coming

   D humidity

8 Although you use a computer, you should still practice your handwriting.

   F although

   G practice

   H computer

   (J) handwriting

9 An earthquake destroyed many structures in that region.

   (A) earthquake

   B region

   C structures

   D destroyed

10 The lightning frightened the children during the thunderstorm.

   (F) thunderstorm

   G lightning

   H children

   J frightened

11 Bob wrote a poem about the splendid sunset he observed one June evening.

   A evening

   B observed

   (C) sunset

   D splendid

12 Nell's volleyball team played an exhibition game in the community stadium.

   F exhibition

   G stadium

   H community

   (J) volleyball

GO ON

Common Core State Standards

Questions 7–12: CCSS Foundational Skills 3.a. Use combined knowledge of all letter-sound correspondences, syllabication patterns, and morphology (e.g., roots and affixes) to read accurately unfamiliar multisyllabic words in context and out of context.

COMPREHENSION

Monster Hurricanes

Hurricanes are large storms that form over warm waters. They can move in over land, causing damage to trees, buildings, and even landforms such as islands. Not all hurricanes are equal, however.

When conditions are just right, huge hurricanes can form. Luckily these powerful storms do not happen too often. It is even less likely for them to hit land because the waters near shorelines get stirred up and bring cooler water to the surface. To stay powerful, hurricanes need very warm water.

The U.S. Weather Bureau has a scale to measure the power of hurricanes. It is called the Saffir-Simpson Scale. As you can see in the chart, the higher the number, the stronger the storm.

Saffir-Simpson Scale for Hurricanes

Category	Maximum Sustained Wind Speed (mph)	Description of Damage
1	74–96	minimal
2	97–111	moderate
3	112–131	extensive
4	132–155	extreme
5	156+	catastrophic

Since the 1930s, only two Category 5 hurricanes have struck land in the United States. One of these was Hurricane Camille in 1969.

Hurricane Camille started out in the Caribbean Sea as a weak storm. When it moved over the warm waters of the Gulf of Mexico, it strengthened quickly. By the time this storm was nearing landfall in Mississippi, it had winds of 200 miles per hour (mph). No one knows for sure how fast it was, because no weather instruments can hold up in winds that strong. Camille also drove a wall of water more than 22 feet tall into the coast of Mississippi. That is the highest storm tide ever seen in the United States.

The town of Pass Christian, Mississippi, was almost completely destroyed. Even towns nearly 100 miles inland from the coast were hard-hit. One such town—Columbia, Mississippi—recorded winds of 120 mph.

Camille weakened as it moved in further over land, but its rains caused flooding over many states. Although other storms have caused greater damage and loss of life, Hurricane Camille still holds the record for fastest wind speed and greatest storm tide.

GO ON

Directions

Choose the item that best answers each question about the selection you just read. Circle the letter next to the answer.

13 How does this author define *hurricane*?

  A a tornado over land

  (B) a large storm over water

  C an unnamed storm

  D hot, dry winds from the tropics

14 During Hurricane Camille, the residents of Columbia, Mississippi, experienced winds of

  F Category 1 strength.

  G Category 2 strength.

  (H) Category 3 strength.

  J Category 4 strength.

15 A hurricane with maximum wind speeds of 154 mph would be considered

  (A) a Category 4 storm.

  B a Category 1 storm.

  C a Category 2 storm.

  D a Category 3 storm.

16 Why does the author include the Saffir-Simpson Scale in the article?

  F to convince readers that all hurricanes are bad

  G to show that most hurricanes are not dangerous

  H to explain how hurricanes form

  (J) to put the information about hurricane strength in an easy-to-read format

17 To remain very powerful, a hurricane needs to

  (A) stay over very warm water.

  B move over land.

  C run into mountains.

  D stay over cool water.

18 What word best describes the power of a Category 5 storm, such as Camille?

  F minimal

  G moderate

  H extreme

  (J) catastrophic

19 Down to what speed could Camille's wind fall before it is no longer considered a hurricane?

  A 0 mph

  B 155 mph

  (C) 73 mph

  D 156 mph

20 The author's purpose in this passage is to

  F persuade readers to take precautions when a hurricane is near.

  G entertain readers with amazing personal stories of surviving a hurricane.

  H express an opinion about the accuracy of hurricane forecasters.

  (J) inform readers about a historically powerful hurricane.

GO ON

Common Core State Standards

Question 13: CCSS Informational Text 1. Quote accurately from a text when explaining what the text says explicitly and when drawing inferences from the text. **Questions 14–16, 18–19: CCSS Informational Text 7.** Draw on information from multiple print or digital sources, demonstrating the ability to locate an answer to a question quickly or to solve a problem efficiently. **Question 17: CCSS Informational Text 2.** Determine two or more main ideas of a text and explain how they are supported by key details; summarize the text. **Question 20: CCSS Informational Text 8.** Explain how an author uses reasons and evidence to support particular points in a text, identifying which reasons and evidence support which point(s).

WRITTEN RESPONSE TO THE SELECTION

Look Back and Write Look back at pages 456–463. The selection shows how artists use special effects to re-create dinosaurs and landscapes. Write a summary of how special-effects artists make movies look so realistic. Provide evidence from the text to support your answer.

The information in the box below will help you remember what you should think about when you write your composition.

REMEMBER—YOU SHOULD

☐ summarize how special-effects artists make movies look so realistic.

☐ briefly explain what a special-effects artist is.

☐ make sure you include only important details as you summarize the text.

☐ organize your ideas clearly and logically so the reader can follow your composition.

☐ check your work for correct spelling, capitalization, punctuation, grammar, and sentences.

GO ON

Common Core State Standards

CCSS Writing 2. Write informative/explanatory texts to examine a topic and convey ideas and information clearly. (Also **CCSS Writing 4.**, **CCSS Language 1.**)

VOCABULARY

Directions

Find the word or words with the same meaning as the underlined word. Circle the letter next to the answer.

1 He watched with <u>envy</u> as she left for her vacation.

  A annoyance

  (B) jealousy

  C frustration

  D enjoyment

2 They were <u>fleeing</u> the building.

  F damaging

  G sketching

  (H) escaping

  J touring

3 The film's plot was <u>complex</u>.

  (A) hard to understand

  B peculiar

  C suspenseful

  D easy to predict

4 He won the game because of his <u>strategy</u>.

  F concentration

  G bravery

  H dedication

  (J) planning

5 His <u>blunders</u> amused her.

  A suggestions

  B beliefs

  (C) mistakes

  D methods

6 The sunrise <u>inspired</u> the artists.

  (F) caused them to create

  G exhausted

  H caused them to wake up

  J fascinated

7 She heard an animal <u>rustling</u> in the bushes.

  A fighting an enemy

  (B) making a soft sound

  C running quickly

  D finding prey

Common Core State Standards

Questions 1–7: CCSS Language 5.c. Use the relationship between particular words (e.g., synonyms, antonyms, homographs) to better understand each of the words.

WORD ANALYSIS OPTIONAL SUBTEST

*D*irections
Find the word that completes each sentence. Circle the letter next to the answer.

8 Jan _____ all the video games Saul had.

(F) envied

G envying

H enving

J envyed

9 The suspects _____ the scene of the robbery.

A fleeing

(B) fled

C flees

D fleed

10 Try not to _____ your lines during the performance.

F blunders

G blundering

H blundered

(J) blunder

11 I tried to _____ Marie to run for office.

A inspires

B inspiring

(C) inspire

D inspired

12 Yesterday the students were _____ in their seats before the final bell rang.

F shifted

(G) shifting

H shift

J shifts

GO ON

⎛ **Common Core State Standards** ⎞

Questions 8–12: CCSS Language 1. Demonstrate command of the conventions of standard English grammar and usage when writing or speaking.

COMPREHENSION

Rescuing Steve

The impatient knocking grew louder on Matthew's bedroom door. He rolled over and checked his alarm clock. It was 6:00 A.M. on Saturday morning.

Matthew groaned as he got out of bed and groggily opened the door. Steve, his big brother, was already dressed in jeans and a hooded sweatshirt. Matthew could tell that he was annoyed and wanted to get going.

"Get dressed quickly," Steve told him, "or we'll be late. Trout don't bite all morning!"

Steve was taking Matthew trout fishing for the first time. Steve had just gotten some new fishing gear, and he was excited to teach Matthew how to trout fish.

They walked along a trail in the woods. The sun was just rising, and Matthew could smell pine needles in the morning air. Steve carried a tackle box and two fishing rods while Matthew carried a small cooler. The trail ended at a ledge overlooking a wide stream. Everything was quiet except for the sound of the water rushing over rocks. Morning dew glistened on green leaves overhead.

Steve began setting up his fishing gear. When he was done, he handed one of the fishing rods to Matthew. "Want me to show you how to cast?" he asked. "It's a little tricky."

Before Matthew could answer, Steve climbed down the ledge. He stood on a large boulder and moved the rod over his head and behind him. "See, it's like this," he called back to Matthew, bending his elbow. "It goes behind your head and then forward. It's like serving in tennis."

Suddenly Steve slipped, and before Matthew knew what was happening, Steve fell into the stream.

Matthew slid down the ledge into the water. The stream was cold and almost up to his neck. He made his way around the boulder and saw Steve hanging onto another smaller rock. He looked scared.

"Grab my hand!" he told Steve. "I won't let you go. I promise." Steve took hold of Matthew's hand. Slowly but surely, Matthew pulled his big brother to safety.

"That was close," Steve said when they were back on land. "I'm glad you came with me. Thanks!"

"No problem," Matthew told him, letting out a heavy sigh. "That's what little brothers are for."

GO ON

Directions

Choose the item that best answers each question about the selection you just read. Circle the letter next to the answer.

13 Based on the passage, you can conclude that Matthew and Steve

    A don't enjoy spending time together.

    B are mean to each other.

    C never go places together.

    (D) often do things together.

14 Based on the passage, why is Steve annoyed at Matthew before they go fishing?

    (F) Matthew hasn't gotten out of bed yet.

    G Matthew is better at fishing than his brother.

    H Matthew won't tell him how to get to the stream.

    J Matthew won't let him use his fishing rod when they get to the stream.

15 The phrase "groggily opened the door" means that Matthew

    A liked opening doors.

    (B) was not fully awake.

    C was afraid of opening doors.

    D did not want to talk to his brother.

16 Why did the author include paragraph 5 in the passage?

    F to show what a trout looks like

    G to show the relationship between Matthew and Steve

    (H) to show the setting of the story

    J to show how to catch a fish

17 The main purpose of the last four paragraphs is to show

    A how to hike in the woods.

    B how Steve and Matthew learn to fish together.

    C how to catch a trout.

    (D) how Matthew rescues Steve.

18 What would most likely have happened if Matthew had *not* rescued Steve?

    (F) Steve would have gotten sick or injured.

    G Steve would have gone fishing with someone else.

    H Steve would have continued fishing from the smaller rock.

    J Steve would have gone to a different fishing spot.

19 How do Matthew and Steve feel at the end of the passage?

    A Matthew is tired, and Steve is annoyed.

    (B) Matthew is relieved, and Steve is grateful.

    C Matthew is bored, and Steve is excited.

    D Matthew is annoyed, and Steve is scared.

20 Which sentence best states the theme of the story?

    F Big brothers always know best.

    G New things bring surprises.

    H Some people always mess things up.

    (J) Brothers should help each other.

GO ON

Common Core State Standards

Questions 13–14, 16–18: CCSS Literature 1. Quote accurately from a text when explaining what the text says explicitly and when drawing inferences from the text. **Question 15: CCSS Literature 4.** Determine the meaning of words and phrases as they are used in a text, including figurative language such as metaphors and similes. **Questions 19–20: CCSS Literature 2.** Determine a theme of a story, drama, or poem from details in the text, including how characters in a story or drama respond to challenges or how the speaker in a poem reflects upon a topic; summarize the text.

WRITTEN RESPONSE TO THE SELECTION

> **Look Back and Write** Look at the picture on pages 36–37. Then read the story's final sentence. Explain how the words make a surprise ending to *Weslandia*. Provide evidence to support your answer.

The information in the box below will help you remember what you should think about when you write your composition.

REMEMBER—YOU SHOULD

☐ explain how the story's final sentence gives *Weslandia* a surprise ending.

☐ compare and contrast the beginning of the story with its ending.

☐ organize your ideas clearly as you write so that your reader understands what you are saying.

☐ use details from the story as evidence to support your answer.

☐ check your work for correct spelling, capitalization, punctuation, grammar, and sentences.

GO ON

⌐ **Common Core State Standards** ⌐

CCSS Writing 9. Draw evidence from literary or informational texts to support analysis, reflection, and research. (Also **CCSS Literature 1.**, **CCSS Writing 4.**, **CCSS Writing 5.**, **CCSS Writing 9.a.**, **CCSS Writing 10.**, **CCSS Language 1.**, **CCSS Language 2.**)

VOCABULARY

Directions

Find the word or words with the same meaning as the underlined word. Circle the letter next to the answer.

1 I always wanted a **Dalmatian** for a pet.

   A certain breed of cat

   B certain breed of horse

   Ⓒ certain breed of dog

   D certain breed of rabbit

2 Fuji came home from the game with a **sprained** ankle.

   F bruised and sore

   G mended and healed

   Ⓗ wrenched and twisted

   J snapped and broken

3 The tourists were **promenading** along the boardwalk.

   Ⓐ strolling

   B racing

   C hopping

   D sitting

4 Violet wore her **frilly** dress.

   F plaid

   G striped

   Ⓗ ruffled

   J woolen

5 We had a **substitute** teacher for algebra class today.

   A confused

   B inexperienced

   C expert

   Ⓓ replacement

GO ON

Common Core State Standards

Questions 1–5: CCSS Language 5.c. Use the relationship between particular words (e.g., synonyms, antonyms, homographs) to better understand each of the words.

WORD ANALYSIS OPTIONAL SUBTEST

Directions

Find the word whose meaning best completes each sentence. Circle the letter next to the answer.

6 The doctor _____ ran to the victim's aid.

- (F) quickly
- G quickest
- H quicker
- J quicken

7 The _____ amazed the audience with his tricks.

- A magic
- (B) magician
- C magical
- D magically

8 My brother wants to be a _____ when he grows up.

- F musical
- G musicianship
- H musically
- (J) musician

9 The batter hit a _____ long fly ball.

- A terrific
- B terror
- (C) terrifically
- D errified

10 Eddie worked as a radio _____ during the summers.

- (F) technician
- G technical
- H technology
- J technically

11 The camel plodded _____ across the sands.

- A silent
- (B) silently
- C silence
- D silences

12 Pam could decorate a cake more _____ than anyone else.

- F artisan
- G artistic
- (H) artistically
- J artist

COMPREHENSION

Turtle and Rhino

One hot, dry afternoon Turtle met Rhino at the local watering hole. The two friends greeted one another warmly. Rhino asked, "What's that on your back?"

Turtle was struggling to carry a large cloth-wrapped bundle on his shell.

"Those are my drums," said Turtle. "I'm playing at the party tonight that Crocodile is throwing for Rattlesnake."

GO ON

Common Core State Standards

Questions 6–12: CCSS Language 5.c. Use the relationship between particular words (e.g., synonyms, antonyms, homographs) to better understand each of the words.

"How exciting!" said Rhino. "I'm going to the party too, so let's go together."

Rhino took a refreshing dip in the water, and Turtle took a long, cool drink to soothe his dry throat. Then they set out for the party. Turtle, of course, moved very slowly, which suited Rhino just fine. No animal liked to move quickly in the awful heat.

As they trudged along the dusty path, they talked about the party and the friends they expected to see. They both knew and liked Rattlesnake—and Crocodile's Reptile Band was known for many miles around. It was bound to be the party of the year.

Rhino was eager to hear the music and looked forward to the company. Many of the animals lived far apart, so they were only able to meet once in a while. Tonight they would all gather under the stars.

The shadows grew longer and darkness began to fall as the two friends finally arrived at the party. Some animals were stringing colored lights from tree to tree, while others were setting up the stage for the band. There would be places to eat, dance, or just to relax and talk. Rhino couldn't contain himself when he saw this last area by the watering place. He was not a good dancer, but he could sure talk the night away. He was bound to have a wonderful night.

Turtle plodded over to the stage to unwrap and set up his drums for rehearsal. Crocodile, Lizard, and the other musicians greeted him with loud shouts of joy.

Soon the brightly-colored lights were glowing in the darkness and animals were dancing to the music of the Reptile Band. The festival was on!

During a lively conversation with Lion, Rhino glanced toward the band. Turtle caught his eye and the two friends smiled at each other. Both enjoyed the party, but it was nice to think of the long walk home together tomorrow. They would talk quietly and enjoy each other's company.

GO ON

Directions

Choose the item that best answers each question about the selection you just read. Circle the letter next to the answer.

13 Which of the following statements from the story is a generalization?

  A   It was a hot, dry afternoon.

  (B) No animal liked to run in the heat.

  C   They talked about the party.

  D   The shadows grew longer.

14 From the story, you might generalize that

  (F) everyone enjoys going to parties.

  G   every party has places to eat, dance, and talk.

  H   most rhinos are not good dancers.

  J   animals like to celebrate weddings.

15 From the information in paragraph 8, you can conclude that

  (A) everyone will have a great time at the party.

  B   old friends won't have time to get together.

  C   there won't be any music at the party.

  D   the animals won't be able to see each other in the dark.

16 What does Turtle do when he reaches the place where the party is being held?

  (F) He sets up his drums.

  G   He strings up lights in the trees.

  H   He has a conversation with Lion.

  J   He smiles at Rhino.

17 Which statement is a generalization?

  A   The two friends smiled at each other.

  B   Others were setting up the stage for the band.

  C   The festival was on!

  (D) Many of the animals lived far apart.

18 From the information in paragraph 8, you might make the generalization that

  (F) rhinos are not good dancers.

  G   parties aren't usually thrown at night.

  H   crocodiles like water better than land.

  J   rattlesnakes are good at playing drums.

19 Which statement is a generalization?

  A   What's that on your back?

  (B) I always like parties.

  C   Let me travel with you.

  D   Those are my drums.

20 This story probably takes place in

  F   winter.

  G   spring.

  (H) summer.

  J   fall.

Common Core State Standards

Questions 13–20: CCSS Literature 1. Quote accurately from a text when explaining what the text says explicitly and when drawing inferences from the text.

WRITTEN RESPONSE TO THE SELECTION

> **Look Back and Write** Look back at pages 59–60 and pages 66–67. How do events described on pages 59–60 and pages 66–67 connect to each other? Provide evidence from the story to support your answer.

The information in the box below will help you remember what you should think about when you write your composition.

REMEMBER—YOU SHOULD

☐ explain how events described on pages 59–60 and pages 66–67 in the story connect to each other.

☐ review the text to draw conclusions about the events in the story before you begin to write.

☐ summarize events in the story in your own words.

☐ communicate your ideas clearly so that the reader really understands how the events are connected.

☐ check your work for correct spelling, capitalization, punctuation, grammar, and sentences.

GO ON

Common Core State Standards

CCSS Writing 9. Draw evidence from literary or informational texts to support analysis, reflection, and research. (Also **CCSS Literature 1.**, **CCSS Writing 4.**, **CCSS Writing 5.**, **CCSS Language 1.**, **CCSS Language 2.**)

VOCABULARY

Directions

Find the word or words with the same meaning as the underlined word. Circle the letter next to the answer.

1 Listening to music <u>enables</u> us to relax.

    A nudges

    (B) makes it possible for

    C cautions

    D makes it difficult for

2 Tigers are <u>scarce</u> in this area.

    (F) not plentiful

    G extinct

    H not curious

    J eerie

3 Both plants and animals <u>specialize</u> in order to survive.

    A grow big and strong

    B cool off during hot weather

    (C) adapt to an environment

    D become different colors

4 Water is <u>critical</u> to living creatures.

    F unfamiliar

    G enjoyable

    H satisfying

    (J) necessary

5 This medicine reduces the production of <u>mucus</u>.

    A liquid that carries oxygen through the body

    B the outer layer of the body

    (C) thick substance made in the body

    D the inner frame of the body

6 The bandage is <u>sterile</u>.

    (F) clean

    G crinkled

    H unraveled

    J tight

GO ON

Common Core State Standards

Questions 1–6: CCSS Language 5.c. Use the relationship between particular words (e.g., synonyms, antonyms, homographs) to better understand each of the words.

WORD ANALYSIS

Directions

Find the word or words with the same meaning as the underlined word. Circle the letter next to the answer.

7 We should <u>summarize</u> the results of the experiment.

   Ⓐ sum up

   B sell

   C send out

   D arrange

8 He is ready to <u>apologize</u> for his mistake.

   F tell others about

   G defend

   Ⓗ admit he was wrong

   J repeat

9 Her signature will <u>finalize</u> the deal.

   A postpone

   B inspire

   C cancel

   Ⓓ complete

10 Kim's dogs always <u>terrorize</u> her neighbors.

   F annoy

   G disagree with

   Ⓗ greatly frighten

   J entertain

11 The company wants her to <u>itemize</u> her expenses.

   A increase

   Ⓑ list

   C deposit

   D destroy

12 He does not like to <u>criticize</u> other people.

   F tease

   Ⓖ find fault with

   H sit next to

   J travel with

GO ON

Common Core State Standards

Questions 7–12: CCSS Language 5.c. Use the relationship between particular words (e.g., synonyms, antonyms, homographs) to better understand each of the words.

COMPREHENSION
The United States and Canada: A World of Difference

The United States and Canada share one of the world's longest borders. But while there are many similarities between the two countries, there are also differences. These include differences in total population, people, and weather.

Canada is a much bigger country than the United States, yet the population of the U.S is about ten times as large. Many people in both countries live in cities. However, most of the major cities in Canada are near the U.S. border. In the United States, major cities are spread throughout the country.

Despite this difference, many cities in both the U.S. and Canada are near large bodies of water. Toronto and Chicago are near the Great Lakes. Vancouver and Los Angeles are near the Pacific Ocean. Halifax and Miami are close to the Atlantic Ocean.

The history of both countries is a story of migration. The earliest settlers in both countries were immigrants. But today most immigrants in Canada come from Asian countries such as India, the Philippines, and Vietnam. Most immigrants in the United States come from Mexico, Russia, and China.

There are also big differences in weather between the two countries. In the U.S., different parts of the country have different climates. By contrast, the weather in Canada tends to be cold. Canadian summers are short and cool, but the days are long. Winters are bitterly cold. Frost can happen at any time of the year.

Although most people think of Canada as a "cold" country, a part of the United States has similar conditions. This weather is found in Alaska. Alaska is the largest state in the U.S. in terms of size, but it has one of its smallest populations.

The United States and Canada: Facts and Figures

	United States	Canada
Area	3,539,225 sq mi	3,855,102 sq mi
Population	approx. 303 million	approx. 33 million
Major Sources of Immigration	Mexico, Russia, China	India, Vietnam, Philippines
Weather	Varies by region	Cold—summers tend to be short
Major Languages Spoken	English 82% Spanish 11%	English 59% French 23%

GO ON

Directions

Choose the item that best answers each question about the selection you just read. Circle the letter next to the answer.

13 The chart helps the reader

    A quickly locate the U.S. and Canada.

    B learn about the history of the U.S. and Canada.

    Ⓒ recognize differences between the U.S. and Canada.

    D know about the economies of the U.S. and Canada.

14 Based on the chart, many U.S. immigrants are

    F French.

    G Vietnamese.

    H Indian.

    Ⓙ Mexican.

15 Information in the chart supports the idea that

    A Canada has a larger population than the U.S.

    B the U.S. and Canada are the same size.

    C the U.S and Canada have similar weather.

    Ⓓ the U.S. has a larger population than Canada.

16 Based on the chart, Canada could best be described as

    Ⓕ large and cold.

    G small and warm.

    H large and warm.

    J small and cold.

17 Why did the author include paragraph 3 in the selection?

    A to show similarities between U.S. and Canadian weather

    B to show differences between U.S. and Canadian history

    Ⓒ to show similarities between U.S. and Canadian cities

    D to show how the U.S. and Canada work together

18 The chart shows that most people in Canada speak

    F French.

    G Spanish.

    Ⓗ English.

    J Vietnamese.

19 The U.S. state that is most similar to Canada is

    A Maine.

    Ⓑ Alaska.

    C Minnesota.

    D Hawaii.

20 The main idea of this passage is that

    Ⓕ the U.S. and Canada share a border but have differences.

    G the U.S. and Canada share a border and are similar.

    H the U.S. and Canada have similar weather.

    J the U.S. and Canada share goods and services.

GO ON

Common Core State Standards

Questions 13–16, 18: CCSS Informational Text 7. Draw on information from multiple print or digital sources, demonstrating the ability to locate an answer to a question quickly or to solve a problem efficiently. **Question 17: CCSS Informational Text 1.** Quote accurately from a text when explaining what the text says explicitly and when drawing inferences from the text. **Questions 19–20: CCSS Informational Text 2.** Determine two or more main ideas of a text and explain how they are supported by key details; summarize the text.

WRITTEN RESPONSE TO THE SELECTION

> **Look Back and Write** Review the facts on pages 88–89. Exactly how do soldier ants operate? Provide evidence to support your answer.

The information in the box below will help you remember what you should think about when you write your composition.

REMEMBER—YOU SHOULD

- ☐ explain how soldier ants operate.

- ☐ use time-order words when explaining a sequence of events.

- ☐ use descriptive words to help your reader visualize what you are saying.

- ☐ make sure that each sentence you write helps the reader understand your composition.

- ☐ check your work for correct spelling, capitalization, punctuation, grammar, and sentences.

> **Common Core State Standards**

CCSS Writing 2. Write informative/explanatory texts to examine a topic and convey ideas and information clearly.
(Also **CCSS Informational Text 1., CCSS Writing 4., CCSS Writing 5., CCSS Language 1., CCSS Language 2.**)

_____

_____

_____

_____

_____

_____

_____

_____

_____

_____

_____

_____

_____

_____

_____

_____

_____

_____

_____

_____

_____

_____

_____

Name _____

VOCABULARY

Directions

Find the word or words with the same meaning as the underlined word. Circle the letter next to the answer.

1 The final <u>episode</u> will be shown on Friday night.

   Ⓐ part of a series

   B act of a play

   C script

   D commercial

2 The cook <u>demonstrates</u> how to make bread.

   F memorizes

   G wonders

   Ⓗ shows

   J transforms

3 He wanted to increase the company's <u>profile</u> in the southeast.

   A power

   B money earned

   C property

   Ⓓ public image

4 I do not have any <u>cavities</u>.

   F freckles

   Ⓖ holes in teeth

   H scrapes

   J broken bones

5 Our teacher is <u>strict</u>.

   Ⓐ tough

   B brilliant

   C determined

   D easygoing

6 Mike always forgets his <u>combination</u>.

   F spoken lines in a play

   G bin location

   Ⓗ set of numbers to open a lock

   J committee meeting

Common Core State Standards

Questions 1–6: CCSS Language 5.c. Use the relationship between particular words (e.g., synonyms, antonyms, homographs) to better understand each of the words.

WORD ANALYSIS

Directions

Find the word with the same meaning as the underlined word. Circle the letter next to the answer.

7 I <u>commiserated</u> with Jean after the impossible test.

   A ignored

   (B) sympathized with

   C spoke with

   D criticized

8 The strong wind will <u>propel</u> the sailboat across the bay.

   F overturn

   G slow down

   (H) push forward

   J change the direction of

9 The book's <u>epilogue</u> was very short.

   A opening section

   B middle section

   C text between sections

   (D) last section

10 Evan <u>compressed</u> the stack of shirts so they would fit into his suitcase.

   (F) squeeze together

   G pushed away

   H committed to memory

   J paid no attention to

11 She tries to be <u>professional</u> in her job.

   A hardworking

   B creative

   (C) businesslike

   D determined

12 The <u>epigram</u> at the beginning of the book was confusing.

   F title page

   (G) short poem

   H first chapter

   J author's note

GO ON

Common Core State Standards

Questions 7–12: CCSS Language 4.b. Use common, grade-appropriate Greek and Latin affixes and roots as clues to the meaning of a word (e.g., *photograph, photosynthesis*).

COMPREHENSION

The Maya

The Maya Indians lived in Mexico for thousands of years before the Spanish explorers arrived in the 1500s. They achieved many great things. They had farms, beautiful palaces, and cities with many buildings. The Mayan people knew a lot about nature and the world around them. This helped them live a better life than most people of that time.

The Maya believed in many gods, such as rain gods, sun gods, and corn gods. The people built large temples to honor the Mayan gods. Workers built cities around these temples. It was hard for them to build these cities. They had no horses to carry the heavy stone they used for building. Workers had to carry all of the materials themselves. Today, many of these Mayan cities and temples are still standing.

The cities that the Maya built were beautiful, and the people worked hard to build them. But very few people lived in them. Usually, only the priests lived in the cities.

Everyone else lived in small villages in the forests. Their houses were much simpler. They lived in small huts with no windows. The walls were made of poles covered with dried mud. The roof was made of grass or leaves. Most Mayans lived simple lives close to nature.

Measuring time was important to the Maya. Farmers needed to know when to plant and harvest their crops. Mayan priests made a system to keep track of time. They wrote numbers as dots (...) and bars (—). A dot meant one, and a bar meant five.

The Mayan priests studied the sun, moon, stars, and planets. They made a calendar from what they learned. The year was divided into eighteen months of twenty days each, with five days left over.

Around the year 800, the Maya left their villages and beautiful cities, never to return. No one knows why this happened. They may have died from a disease. They may have left because the soil could no longer grow crops. Scientists are still trying to find the lost secrets of the Maya. They are still one of our greatest mysteries.

GO ON

Directions

Choose the item that best answers each question about the selection you just read. Circle the letter next to the answer.

13 What generalization is made in paragraph 1?

   A All Mayan people had beautiful farms.

   B Many Mayan people were priests.

   (C) The Mayan people lived a better life than most people of that time.

   D No one knows why the Mayan people disappeared.

14 What details are used to support the generalization in paragraph 1?

   F The Mayan priests studied the sun, moon, stars, and planets.

   G Only the priests lived in the cities.

   H The Spanish arrived in Mexico in the 1500s.

   (J) The Maya knew a lot about nature and the world around them.

15 What conclusion can you draw about the Mayan people in paragraph 5?

   A They stopped growing crops because they wanted to eat meat.

   B They were not very advanced.

   C Life was very unfair in Mayan society.

   (D) Math was important to their everyday lives.

16 What generalization is made in paragraph 4?

   (F) Most Mayans lived a simple life close to nature.

   G Many of these Mayan cities and temples are still standing.

   H The people worked hard to build cities.

   J The people lived in small huts with no windows.

17 Measuring time was important to the Maya because

   A they lived close to nature.

   (B) farmers needed to know when to plant their crops.

   C the Mayan gods told them it was important.

   D they needed to know when to leave work.

18 What details support the generalization that the Maya are still one of our greatest mysteries?

   F They had no horses to carry the heavy stone they used for building.

   G The cities that the Maya built were beautiful.

   (H) Scientists are still trying to find the lost secrets of the Maya.

   J Many of these Mayan cities and temples are still standing.

19 What generalization is made in the last paragraph?

   A The Maya may have died from disease.

   B All Mayan people measured time.

   (C) No one knows why the Maya disappeared.

   D All Mayan cities were beautiful.

20 The Maya honored their gods by

   (F) building great temples.

   G living in simple huts.

   H creating a system to measure time.

   J growing special crops.

GO ON

Common Core State Standards

Questions 13–16, 18–19: **CCSS Informational Text 1.** Quote accurately from a text when explaining what the text says explicitly and when drawing inferences from the text. **Questions 17, 20: CCSS Informational Text 2.** Determine two or more main ideas of a text and explain how they are supported by key details; summarize the text.

WRITTEN RESPONSE TO THE SELECTION

> **Look Back and Write** Go back to scene 4 on pages 120–121. What is Hannah's passion and why? Provide evidence to support your answer.

The information in the box below will help you remember what you should think about when you write your composition.

REMEMBER—YOU SHOULD

☐   explain what Hannah's passion is and why it is her passion.

☐   draw conclusions about Hannah based on her words and actions before you begin to write.

☐   use details from the story to support your answer.

☐   make sure that your ideas are clear and easy for the reader to follow.

☐   check your work for correct spelling, capitalization, punctuation, grammar, and sentences.

GO ON

Common Core State Standards

CCSS Writing 9.a. Apply grade 5 Reading standards to literature (e.g., "Compare and contrast two or more characters, settings, or events in a story or a drama, drawing on specific details in the text [e.g., how characters interact]"). (Also **CCSS Literature 1.**, **CCSS Literature 2.**, **CCSS Writing 4.**, **CCSS Writing 5.**, **CCSS Writing 10.**, **CCSS Language 1.**, **CCSS Language 2.**)

_____

_____

_____

_____

_____

_____

_____

_____

_____

_____

_____

_____

_____

_____

_____

_____

_____

_____

_____

_____

VOCABULARY

*D*irections

Find the word or words with the same meaning as the underlined word. Circle the letter next to the answer.

1 Lakesha loves the <u>limelight</u>.
- (A) public attention
- B glistening skyline
- C award ceremonies
- D green sparkles

2 After a brief <u>hesitation</u>, she jumped into the pool.
- F argument
- (G) pause
- H glance
- J incident

3 My brother loves to <u>somersault</u>.
- A complain
- B stand on his head
- C mutter
- (D) perform a rolling movement

4 She completed three <u>cartwheels</u>.
- F travel journals
- G belly flops
- H bicycle trips
- (J) sideways handsprings

5 His head was <u>throbbing</u>.
- A dripping
- B holding
- (C) pounding
- D twitching

6 He was <u>wincing</u> after he fell off his bike.
- (F) making a pained expression
- G sobbing
- H bluish
- J lying facedown on the ground

7 The tires <u>skidded</u> on the wet road.
- A gripped well
- (B) slid without rolling
- C stopped moving
- D lost air

> **Common Core State Standards**

Questions 1–7: CCSS Language 5.c. Use the relationship between particular words (e.g., synonyms, antonyms, homographs) to better understand each of the words.

WORD ANALYSIS

Directions

Find the word or words with the closest meaning to the underlined idiom. Circle the letter next to the answer.

8 **Joe found himself <u>between a rock and a hard place</u>.**

   F working with dirty hands

   (G) having to chose between difficult choices

   H late to an important event

   J not having enough wisdom

9 **The food for the party cost her <u>an arm and a leg</u>.**

   A very little money

   (B) a great deal of money

   C twice as much money

   D no money

10 **I was napping with my dog when he jumped up and started barking <u>out of the blue</u>.**

   F quickly and quietly

   G slowly and carefully

   H steadily and loudly

   (J) suddenly and unexpectedly

11 **Leo <u>went out on a limb</u> and promised a raise to all of his employees.**

   A engaged in illegal activity

   (B) put oneself in a risky situation

   C climbed a tree

   D made promises without intending to keep them

12 **He was <u>thrown in the public eye</u> after saving the drowning woman.**

   F blinded by glory

   G found on the rocks

   (H) the center of attention

   J swept downriver without a paddle

COMPREHENSION

Leonardo Da Vinci: The World's Greatest Inventor

Leonardo Da Vinci was a famous artist and inventor. He lived in Italy during the fifteenth century. At the time, many changes were happening. His ideas were part of the changes. He carefully looked at the world around him. He wanted to know how things worked.

GO ON

Common Core State Standards

Questions 8–12: CCSS Language 5.b. Recognize and explain the meaning of common idioms, adages, and proverbs.

Da Vinci was born in 1452. When he was about five years old, he started drawing. Some pictures showed how machines worked. His father showed them to a famous painter. The painter said he would teach Leonardo to paint when he was older.

Da Vinci read and studied. He helped the painter with some of his works. An angel that he painted was very beautiful. After seeing it, the painter was so impressed that he said he would never paint again.

Da Vinci left his home in 1482 because he needed a job. He went to the city of Milan, where he asked the Duke of Milan for work. Da Vinci told the Duke that he could help him improve his navy. The Duke's navy was in very bad shape.

Da Vinci planned weapons and machines for the Duke. He designed a tank with wheels that looked like a turtle. Men could pull it and turn its gun with a crank. He also studied how fish swam. It helped him plan a ship that could go underwater. Hundreds of years later, this idea became a submarine.

In 1495, Da Vinci also designed the world's first robot. The robot looked like a person. It wore a suit of armor. It could wave its arms, move forward, and even move its head! No one is sure if Da Vinci ever built his robot, but his designs helped him study how people move their limbs.

Da Vinci had so many ideas that he started keeping notebooks to help him organize his thoughts. He drew inventions in his notebooks too. He wrote thousands of pages, but most were lost after he died. The pages that are left are full of his mysterious writing. Scientists are still trying to figure out his notebooks today.

Da Vinci stayed in Milan until 1499. Then he traveled across Italy. He wanted to paint again. About four years later he started the *Mona Lisa*, a painting that shows a woman with a bit of a smile. It's one of his most famous works today.

In 1516, the King of France offered Da Vinci a job; he became France's top painter and scientist. He was given a house near the king's palace.

Leonardo died in 1519. The King of France was very sad. The world had lost a true genius.

Directions

Choose the item that best answers each question about the selection you just read. Circle the letter next to the answer.

13 After reading the passage, you can conclude that Leonardo Da Vinci was

   A a lawyer and doctor.

   (B) an artist and inventor.

   C a sculptor and mathematician.

   D an athlete and writer.

14 Why did the painter who saw Leonardo's early work say that he would never paint again?

   F because he was tired of painting

   G because Leonardo made him mad

   (H) because Leonardo's work was so good

   J because he went blind

15 The machines that Da Vinci designed for the Duke of Milan were

   (A) advanced.

   B broken.

   C primitive.

   D silly.

16 You can conclude that the author gives details about Leonardo's robot to show that

   F Leonardo was brave.

   G Leonardo was curious about robots.

   H Leonardo liked building machines.

   (J) Leonardo was ahead of his time.

17 You can conclude that paragraph 7 was written to tell about

   (A) Leonardo's notebooks.

   B Leonardo's inventions.

   C Leonardo's later life.

   D Leonardo's robot.

18 Da Vinci started painting the *Mona Lisa* around

   F 1499.

   (G) 1503.

   H 1516.

   J 1519.

19 The information presented in this passage is organized

   A by comparing and contrasting.

   B by cause and effect.

   (C) in chronological order.

   D with main ideas and support examples.

20 What generalization can you make based on this passage?

   F Leonardo was a great artist but a poor inventor.

   (G) Leonardo's ideas and inventions still influence many people today.

   H Leonardo is only famous in Italy.

   J Leonardo had great ideas, but they never had much of an impact.

GO ON

Common Core State Standards

Questions 13–20: CCSS Informational Text 1. Quote accurately from a text when explaining what the text says explicitly and when drawing inferences from the text.

WRITTEN RESPONSE TO THE SELECTION

Look Back and Write The dog in "The Gymnast" acts as an audience. Find the dog on pages 147 and 151. Why do you think the dog's reaction changes? Why are those details important in understanding "The Gymnast"? Provide evidence to support your answer.

The information in the box below will help you remember what you should think about when you write your composition.

REMEMBER—YOU SHOULD

☐   explain why the dog's reaction changes and why these details are important in understanding the story.

☐   reread both pages carefully to contrast the dog's reactions before you start to write.

☐   use details from the text to support your answer.

☐   make sure that each sentence you write helps the reader understand your composition.

☐   check your work for correct spelling, capitalization, punctuation, grammar, and sentences.

GO ON

Common Core State Standards

CCSS Writing 9.a. Apply grade 5 Reading standards to literature (e.g., "Compare and contrast two or more characters, settings, or events in a story or a drama, drawing on specific details in the text [e.g., how characters interact]"). (Also **CCSS Literature 1.**, **CCSS Writing 4.**, **CCSS Writing 5.**, **CCSS Writing 9.a.**, **CCSS Writing 10.**, **CCSS Language 1.**, **CCSS Language 2.**)

VOCABULARY

Directions

Find the word or words with the same meaning as the underlined word. Circle the letter next to the answer.

1 The spelunkers headed into the <u>cavern</u>.

   A park

   (B) cave

   C river

   D countryside

2 She made an <u>attempt</u> to soothe the baby.

   (F) effort

   G song

   H game

   J face

3 We <u>abandoned</u> the game after an hour.

   A invented

   B started on

   C played through

   (D) gave up on

4 The builder let out a <u>bellow</u>.

   F cry of pain

   G happy laugh

   (H) loud yell

   J secret message

5 That dog looks like a <u>savage</u> animal.

   A friendly

   B playful

   C old

   (D) wild

6 The letter was <u>immensely</u> difficult to read.

   F not at all

   (G) very greatly

   H somewhat

   J equally

7 Walking a tightrope is quite a <u>feat</u>.

   A act of stupidity

   B act of kindness

   (C) act of skill or daring

   D act of carelessness

GO ON

Common Core State Standards

Questions 1–7: CCSS Language 5.c. Use the relationship between particular words (e.g., synonyms, antonyms, homographs) to better understand each of the words.

WORD ANALYSIS

OPTIONAL SUBTEST

Directions

Find the words with the same meaning as the underlined word. Circle the letter next to the answer.

8 We agreed that the outcome was <u>impossible</u>.

   F possible

   G very possible

   Ⓗ not possible

   J unknown

9 We feel it is <u>improper</u> for students to give gifts to teachers.

   A unfair

   B understandable

   Ⓒ not appropriate

   D decent

10 Those details are <u>immaterial</u>.

   F invisible

   G important

   Ⓗ unimportant

   J slightly visible

11 The gulf was <u>immeasurable</u>.

   Ⓐ could not be measured

   B was measured from beneath

   C was measured around

   D was measured together

12 The cat sat <u>immobile</u> as it watched the squirrel.

   Ⓕ motionless

   G quietly

   H smoothly

   J flexible

GO ON

Common Core State Standards

Questions 8–12: CCSS Language 4.b. Use common, grade-appropriate Greek and Latin affixes and roots as clues to the meaning of a word (e.g., photograph, photosynthesis).

Name _____

COMPREHENSION

Soup of the Evening

My friends and I went to a boarding school in Ohio. At our school, students could eat their meals in any of the dining halls. Mark, Chris, Paul, Jean, and I always ate dinner together. It was the best time of the day. Classes were over, and we could relax, talk, and laugh. Our table was next to the windows in one corner of the long room.

You got in line to pick up a tray and silverware. As you went through the line, you loaded your tray with food. It was a good system. We were allowed to eat as much as we wanted.

One evening, most of us were sitting around the table eating hungrily. Paul was running late as usual. When he finally joined us, he was carrying a heavy tray. "You must be extra hungry tonight," said Jean as she moved over to make room for him.

That was when Paul made his big mistake. Instead of keeping his eyes on his tray, he looked at Jean. As he moved forward, the tray tilted. "Watch out!" cried Mark, jumping up, but he was too late. A bowl of soup slid to the edge of the tray and crashed to the floor.

We all laughed. Paul was annoyed, but no one could help laughing. Little accidents like that were always funny. Jean ran for paper towels, and we soon had the mess cleaned up. "Not split pea soup, but SPILLED pea soup," Chris whispered in my ear as we sat down again. I tried to keep a straight face for the rest of the meal, but it wasn't easy.

The next night, Mark and I were the first ones in to dinner. We started talking about the science exam Mark had taken that day. Then Mark suddenly grinned. "Here comes Paul," he said.

I turned to look, and I saw Paul coming toward the table. "He's got soup again!" I said. "And it's split pea again tonight. Do you suppose—"

"No," said Mark. "It could never happen twice."

Just then, Paul got to the table. As we kidded him about the "spilled pea" soup, he asked Mark how the exam had gone. He balanced his tray with one hand while reaching out the other to move his chair. Just then, his bowl of soup slid off his tray and hit the floor.

I did not dare to look at Mark for the rest of the meal. Afterwards, though, we had a good laugh about it!

GO ON

Directions

Choose the item that best answers each question about the selection you just read. Circle the letter next to the answer.

13 Which character is the kindest person?

   A Chris

   (B) Jean

   C Mark

   D the narrator

14 Which word best describes Paul?

   (F) clumsy

   G mean

   H clever

   J silly

15 The events of the plot happen in

   A a kitchen.

   B a restaurant.

   C a classroom.

   (D) a dining hall.

16 What is the most important event of the plot?

   F Jean runs for paper towels.

   G Mark takes a science exam.

   (H) Paul spills his soup.

   J Chris whispers in the narrator's ear.

17 What do all the characters have in common?

   A They are all boys.

   B They are all girls.

   C They all like soup.

   (D) They are all students.

18 Why did the author write this story?

   (F) to entertain

   G to persuade

   H to inform

   J to teach

19 This story is best described as

   A a biography.

   B expository nonfiction.

   (C) realistic fiction.

   D fantasy.

20 What happens just before Jean runs for paper towels?

   F Chris makes a joke about the soup.

   (G) Paul spills the soup.

   H The narrator laughs aloud.

   J Paul asks about Mark's exam.

GO ON

Common Core State Standards

Questions 13, 17: CCSS Literature 3. Compare and contrast two or more characters, settings, or events in a story or drama, drawing on specific details in the text (e.g., how characters interact). **Questions 14–16, 18–20: CCSS Literature 1.** Quote accurately from a text when explaining what the text says explicitly and when drawing inferences from the text.

WRITTEN RESPONSE TO THE SELECTION

> **Look Back and Write** Go back to the story's ending, when the boys are running away from Eddie's father. Do you think the boys will continue to have similar adventures like the one they just had? Write your opinion. Provide evidence to support your answer.

The information in the box below will help you remember what you should think about when you write your composition.

REMEMBER—YOU SHOULD

- ☐ explain if you think the boys will continue to have similar adventures and why.

- ☐ use the boys' words, thoughts, and actions as evidence to support your answer.

- ☐ make sure you explain the events from the story in the correct sequence.

- ☐ state your opinion clearly and provide reasons to support your opinion.

- ☐ check your work for correct spelling, capitalization, punctuation, grammar, and sentences.

⟩ **Common Core State Standards**

CCSS Writing 1. Write opinion pieces on topics or texts, supporting a point of view with reasons and information. (Also **CCSS Writing 5.**, **CCSS Language 1.**)

VOCABULARY

Directions
Find the word or words with the same meaning as the underlined word. Circle the letter next to the answer.

1 There was <u>sediment</u> in the cup.

   A moisture

   B grease

   Ⓒ solid matter that settles at the bottom of a liquid

   D liquid that becomes solid matter

2 The fishing boat uses <u>sonar</u>.

   F large, strong nets

   G a metal object thrown overboard to hold a boat in place

   H a wooden steering wheel

   Ⓙ equipment that uses sound waves to locate underwater objects

3 It was difficult to walk through the <u>debris</u>.

   Ⓐ broken pieces

   B passageway

   C entryway

   D flying objects

4 The <u>robotic</u> toy rolled across the room by itself.

   F well constructed

   G manually operated

   H quickly assembled

   Ⓙ computer controlled

5 The car was <u>cramped</u>.

   A not able to be driven

   B antique

   Ⓒ not having much space

   D expensive

6 She washed the <u>ooze</u> from her feet.

   Ⓕ slimy mud

   G steaming water

   H clear stream

   J dampened dirt

7 The <u>interior</u> of the house was clean.

   A outside

   Ⓑ inside

   C porch

   D balcony

GO ON

Common Core State Standards

Questions 1–7: CCSS Language 5.c. Use the relationship between particular words (e.g., synonyms, antonyms, homographs) to better understand each of the words.

WORD ANALYSIS

Directions
Find the words with the same meaning as the underlined word. Circle the letter next to the answer.

8 Rachel used a <u>laser</u> to cut a hole in the thick board.

   F table saw

   G instrument that uses sound waves to cut

   (H) instrument that focuses light into a strong stream

   J holepunch machine

9 Natalie and Bo carried their <u>scuba</u> gear into the boat.

   (A) device for breathing underwater

   B device for protecting oneself from sharks

   C device for guiding a boat

   D device for catching fish

10 Go to their Web site and look for the <u>FAQs</u> page.

   F Frequently Announced Questions

   G Frequently Added Quotations

   (H) Frequently Asked Questions

   J Frequently Allowed Quicktime

11 Someday doctors may be able to repair <u>DNA</u> to cure sick people.

   A highly complex, expensive medical imaging devices

   (B) the material in cells that encodes information about living things

   C electrical force fields within the body

   D internal structures connecting various organs of the body

12 <u>NASA</u> will launch a new mission to Mars next year.

   F an association of car racers

   G The U.S. Department of Atmospheric Science

   H the name of a launch pad in Florida

   (J) The U.S. Space Administration

COMPREHENSION

The Tragedy of the *Edmund Fitzgerald*

In November of 1975, the freight ship *Edmund Fitzgerald* ran into a bad storm on one of the Great Lakes. The *Edmund Fitzgerald* was built in Detroit, Michigan. It was launched in June of 1958. It was the largest freighter on the Great Lakes at that time. The ship was as long as two football fields.

Common Core State Standards

Questions 8–12: CCSS Language 4. Determine or clarify the meaning of unknown and multiple-meaning words and phrases based on grade 5 reading and content, choosing flexibly from a range of strategies.

On the afternoon of November 9, 1975, the *Edmund Fitzgerald* sailed into Lake Superior. It was loaded with a full cargo and headed for Detroit. The trip would take just three days. Captain Ernest McSorley and his twenty-eight crew members had little reason to fear for their safety.

The ship soon made contact with the *Arthur Anderson*. Its captain was Jessie B. Cooper. The two captains decided to guide their ships together across the lake. A major storm was coming in. The wind was blowing fast on Lake Superior.

During the day of November 10, the storm grew more dangerous. By early evening, the waves were twenty-five feet high. McSorley radioed to Cooper that giant waves had knocked out instruments on the deck of the *Edmund Fitzgerald*. At 7:10 P.M., Cooper asked the *Fitzgerald*'s captain how the ship was doing, and McSorley answered, "We are holding our own." But minutes later, the ship sank.

No one ever heard from the *Edmund Fitzgerald* again. Days later a search plane found the wreck. It was lying on the lake's bottom, 530 feet under water. It had broken in half.

For months, people studied the shipwreck. Some thought that the ship had hit a bump close to the shore, called a *shoal*, that damaged its bottom. Others believed that wave water had flooded the ship's interior from openings on the deck. Evidence found later by divers showed that the ship had sunk very quickly and broken into two parts when it hit bottom. People who believed the wave water idea thought that such a rapid sinking confirmed their view of what had happened. What everyone agreed on was that twenty-nine lives were lost that terrible night.

Name	SS *Edmund Fitzgerald*	Length	729 feet
Launched	June 8, 1958	**Speed**	14 knots
Maiden Voyage	September 24, 1958	**Crew**	29

Directions

Choose the item that best answers each question about the selection you just read. Circle the letter next to the answer.

13 On what date was the *Edmund Fitzgerald* launched?

  A November 10, 1975

  B September 24, 1958

  (C) June 8, 1958

  D November 9, 1975

14 What was the length of the *Edmund Fitzgerald*?

  (F) 729 feet

  G 1,975 feet

  H 625 feet

  J 530 feet

15 What was the maximum speed the *Edmund Fitzgerald* could reach?

  A 29 knots

  B 729 knots

  (C) 14 knots

  D 530 knots

16 How old a ship was the *Edmund Fitzgerald* when it sank?

  F 10 years

  G 13 years

  (H) 17 years

  J 20 years

17 The *Edmund Fitzgerald* went under the waves

  A at 5:30 P.M.

  B at 7:10 P.M.

  (C) minutes after 7:10 P.M.

  D just before midnight.

18 Which of the following statements about the *Edmund Fitzgerald* is correct?

  F Only a few members of its crew were lost in the tragedy.

  (G) All twenty-nine crew members died when the ship sank.

  H The captain of the ship was the only crew member to have died.

  J None of the crew members died when the ship sank.

19 In which lake did the *Edmund Fitzgerald* sink?

  (A) Lake Superior

  B Lake Michigan

  C Lake Erie

  D the Great Lake

20 Which detail does *not* contribute to the main idea of the passage?

  F The wind was blowing fast on Lake Superior.

  G The two captains decided to guide their ships together across the rough water.

  (H) The ship was as long as two football fields.

  J Giant waves knocked out instruments on the deck of the *Edmund Fitzgerald*.

GO ON

> **Common Core State Standards**

Questions 13–16, 18: CCSS Informational Text 7. Draw on information from multiple print or digital sources, demonstrating the ability to locate an answer to a question quickly or to solve a problem efficiently. **Questions 17, 19: CCSS Informational Text 3.** Explain the relationships or interactions between two or more individuals, events, ideas, or concepts in a historical, scientific, or technical text based on specific information in the text. **Question 20: CCSS Informational Text 2.** Determine two or more main ideas of a text and explain how they are supported by key details; summarize the text.

WRITTEN RESPONSE TO THE SELECTION

> **Look Back and Write** Go back to page 213 and reread the section about Willie Coutts. Write a brief diary account told in a first-person voice that describes how Willie was feeling at the time, as he struggled to get on the rescue boat. Provide evidence to support your answer.

The information in the box below will help you remember what you should think about when you write your composition.

REMEMBER—YOU SHOULD

- ☐ explain how Willie Coutts felt as he tried to get on the rescue boat.

- ☐ make sure you write your composition in the first-person voice using such pronouns as *I, me,* and *my.*

- ☐ use descriptive words to explain how Willie felt as he struggled to get on the rescue boat.

- ☐ follow the proper format of a diary entry for your composition.

- ☐ check your work for correct spelling, capitalization, punctuation, grammar, and sentences.

Common Core State Standards

CCSS Writing 9. Draw evidence from literary or informational texts to support analysis, reflection, and research. (Also **CCSS Writing 2.a., CCSS Writing 4., CCSS Language 1.**)

VOCABULARY

Directions
Find the word or words with the same meaning as the underlined word. Circle the letter next to the answer.

1 The students watched the <u>monitors</u>.

   A photographs

   (B) television sets

   C advertisements

   D overhead projections

2 Her <u>role</u> was to be the heroine.

   F desire

   G goal in life

   (H) part in a play or movie

   J challenge

3 Motorcycle riding and French cooking were two of his <u>accomplishments</u>.

   (A) things done with skill

   B things that are fun to do

   C things that are easy to do

   D things that can be done best by men

4 What was the <u>specific</u> cause of your accident?

   F unfortunate

   G preliminary

   (H) exact

   J likely

5 His <u>focus</u> was to have fun.

   (A) main point of interest

   B amusement

   C guiding statement

   D request

6 We learned about <u>gravity</u> in class.

   F scientific methods

   (G) a force that attracts objects toward the center of the Earth

   H current ideas

   J the action of different types of energy

GO ON

Common Core State Standards

Questions 1–6: CCSS Language 5.c. Use the relationship between particular words (e.g., synonyms, antonyms, homographs) to better understand each of the words.

WORD ANALYSIS

Directions
Find the word or words with the same meaning as the underlined word. Circle the letter next to the answer.

7 Kira plans to major in <u>biology</u> in college.

A the study of the stars

B the study of animal life

Ⓒ the study of living things

D the study of rocks and crystals

8 The <u>geologist</u> collected rock samples.

F scientist who studies the air

G scientist who studies space

Ⓗ scientist who studies the earth

J scientist who studies animals

9 Early <u>geographers</u> did not understand where the Atlantic Ocean ended.

Ⓐ people who study land masses and bodies of water

B people who study living things

C people who study rock formations

D people who study how different types of matter interact

10 Jordan would have to take some <u>psychology</u> courses to become a therapist.

F the study of business management

G the study of personal interactions

Ⓗ the study of the mind and human behavior

J the study of foreign languages

11 Our country faced a <u>grave</u> crisis that autumn.

A unnecessary

Ⓑ very serious

C having to do with farms

D forgettable

12 Small children seem to <u>gravitate</u> to the puppet show.

F cry out in fear

G show off

H talk back

Ⓙ move toward as if pulled

GO ON

Common Core State Standards

Questions 7–12: CCSS Language 4.b. Use common, grade-appropriate Greek and Latin affixes and roots as clues to the meaning of a word (e.g., photograph, photosynthesis).

134

Weekly Test 23 Unit 5 Week 3

COMPREHENSION

Our New Library Home: Getting It Right

The Centerville Library Board will hold a public meeting about the new library next Tuesday evening, March 12, at 7:30 P.M. at City Hall. We, the members of the Coalition for a Better Library, will be there. Every interested Centerville citizen should attend.

The Library Board wants to build on a lot at the corner of Route 26 and Kendall Boulevard. Sycamore Mall is diagonally across the intersection. This site was chosen because large numbers of people go to the mall daily. The Library Board thinks the mall traffic will bring people into the library.

The Coalition for a Better Library disagrees. Most people go to the mall just to shop. They are not likely to combine shopping with visiting the library. Also, there is a lot of traffic at that location. Few people will want to walk or drive between the mall and the library.

Our group believes a site closer to the neighborhoods of Centerville would be better. The library does not have to be downtown; it should be closer to where people live. One excellent place might be across the street from Turner Park. We need to think about the elderly and disabled people in our community. City officials have said the proposed library could be added to the mall bus route. However, it seems unlikely that mobility-limited people would make the long trip downtown rather than visit a location closer to home.

This is an important decision for our community! Please attend next Tuesday's meeting or send an e-mail to the head of the Library Board to express your opinion.

GO ON

Directions

Choose the item that best answers each question about the selection you just read. Circle the letter next to the answer.

13 The selection is about

A the problems of the elderly and disabled people in Centerville.

B the Centerville Library Board.

C traffic problems in Centerville.

(D) choosing a location to build a new town library.

14 The writer is speaking on behalf of

F the Centerville Library Board.

G the Sycamore Mall Association.

(H) the Coalition for a Better Library.

J the Coalition of the Elderly.

15 According to the map, which statement is true?

A Downtown Centerville is north of the interstate highway.

(B) Sycamore Mall is next to the exit from the interstate.

C All of Centerville's schools are in the downtown area.

D The proposed library would be miles away from the interstate.

16 Which statement does *not* contribute to the author's purpose?

F People go to the mall just to shop.

G There is a lot of traffic at that location.

H We need to think about the elderly and disabled people.

(J) The proposed library could be added to the mall bus route.

17 How does the author make his point?

A by lying

B by agreeing with the Library Board

(C) by explaining why he thinks the board's ideas will not work

D by telling people to go to the mall instead of the library

18 What reason does the Library Board give for their choice of location?

F It is close to people in two nearby towns.

G The downtown area is in bad shape, so it is best to move further out.

(H) It is near the busy mall.

J It is in a quiet area, far from busy traffic and noise.

19 The author's arguments are

A irrational.

B untrue.

C wrong.

(D) logical.

20 What is the author's purpose in writing this article?

(F) to persuade

G to inform

H to entertain

J to express feelings

GO ON

Common Core State Standards

Questions 13, 18: CCSS Informational Text 2. Determine two or more main ideas of a text and explain how they are supported by key details; summarize the text. **Questions 14, 16–17, 19–20: CCSS Informational Text 8.** Explain how an author uses reasons and evidence to support particular points in a text, identifying which reasons and evidence support which point(s). **Question 15: CCSS Informational Text 7.** Draw on information from multiple print or digital sources, demonstrating the ability to locate an answer to a question quickly or to solve a problem efficiently.

WRITTEN RESPONSE TO THE SELECTION

Look Back and Write Go back to page 238. Why is training harder than the actual space mission? Provide evidence to support your answer.

The information in the box below will help you remember what you should think about when you write your composition.

REMEMBER—YOU SHOULD

☐ explain why training is harder for astronauts than the actual space mission.

☐ compare and contrast training and the space mission in your writing.

☐ include some of Ellen Ochoa's own words in your composition and follow the correct style for quotations.

☐ communicate your ideas clearly so that the reader really understands what you are saying.

☐ check your work for correct spelling, capitalization, punctuation, grammar, and sentences.

GO ON

Common Core State Standards

CCSS Writing 4. Produce clear and coherent writing in which the development and organization are appropriate to task, purpose, and audience. (Also **CCSS Writing 2., CCSS Writing 2.b., CCSS Writing 2.c., CCSS Language 1.**)

Name _____

VOCABULARY

Directions
Find the word or words with the same meaning as the underlined word. Circle the letter next to the answer.

1 The dodo bird is <u>extinct</u>.

(A) no longer existing

B clumsy

C no longer examined

D fascinating

2 The skull <u>encases</u> the brain.

F affects

G damages

(H) encloses

J soothes

3 She thinks that lizards are <u>hideous</u>.

(A) ugly

B remarkable

C amusing

D necessary

4 He wanted to have a <u>serpent</u> as a pet.

F ladybug

(G) snake

H parakeet

J chimpanzee

5 John enjoyed looking at the <u>armor</u> on display.

A primitive weapons

B aircraft

C cannons

(D) protective coverings

6 She <u>plunged</u> her fork into the potato.

F guided

(G) moved downward

H packed

J adjusted sideways

GO ON

> **Common Core State Standards**

Questions 1–6: CCSS Language 5.c. Use the relationship between particular words (e.g., synonyms, antonyms, homographs) to better understand each of the words.

- -

WORD ANALYSIS OPTIONAL SUBTEST

Directions
Choose the correct spelling of the word that completes the blank. Circle the letter next to the word that fills the blank.

7 He was barely _____ when they pulled him from the lake.

   A conshius

   B conscous

   Ⓒ conscious

   D conshus

8 Marla is always a _____ hostess.

   F grascius

   G grashus

   H gracous

   Ⓙ gracious

9 I experienced _____ when my cousin got a new sport car.

   Ⓐ jealousy

   B gelousy

   C gealousy

   D jelosy

10 My mother is the most _____ person I know.

   F couragious

   G couragus

   Ⓗ courageous

   J couragous

11 You look ____ in that dress!

   A gorjus

   Ⓑ gorgeous

   C gorgious

   D gorjeous

12 The _____ singing could be heard for blocks.

   F joyus

   G joyious

   H joyeous

   Ⓙ joyous

COMPREHENSION

Helen Keller

What if you could not see these words or hear them spoken? But you could still talk, write, read, and make friends. In fact, you went to college, wrote nearly a dozen books, went all over the world, met twelve U.S. presidents, and lived to be eighty-seven. Well, there was such a person, and she was born over a hundred years ago!

Meet Helen Keller, a woman from the small farm town of Tuscumbia, Alabama. She taught the world to respect people who are blind and deaf. Her mission came from her own life. When she was one-and-a-half years old, she was extremely ill, and she lost both her vision and hearing. It was like entering a different world with completely new rules,

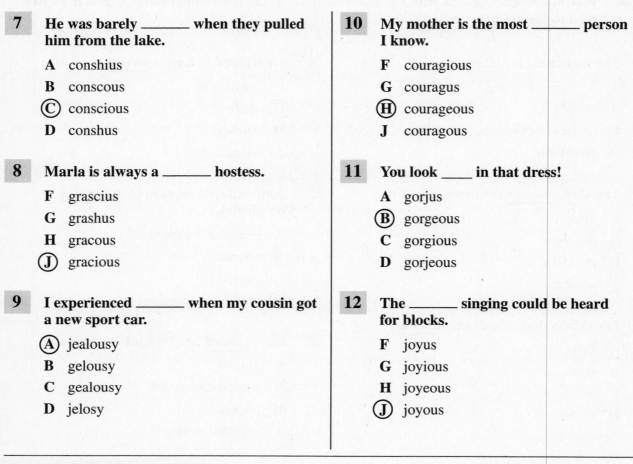

GO ON

⌐ **Common Core State Standards** ⌐

Questions 7–12: CCSS Language 2.e. Spell grade-appropriate words correctly, consulting references as needed.

Name _____

and she got very frustrated. By the time she was seven, her parents knew they needed help. So they hired a tutor named Anne Sullivan.

Anne was strict, but she had a lot of energy. In just a few days, she taught Helen how to spell words with her hands. The trouble was that Helen didn't understand what the words meant—until one morning at the water pump. Anne had Helen hold one hand under the water. Then she spelled W-A-T-E-R into Helen's other hand. The feeling on her palm turned into a word. Immediately Helen bent down and tapped the ground. Anne spelled E-A-R-T-H. Helen's brain flew! That day she learned thirty words.

From then on, Helen's mind raced ahead. She learned to speak when she was ten by feeling her teacher's mouth when she talked. Often people found it hard to understand her, but she never gave up trying. When she was 20, she entered Radcliffe College, the women's branch of Harvard University. A year later she wrote her first book, *The Story of My Life*. She would go on to write ten more books and a lot more articles!

Helen also did research, gave speeches, and helped raise money for many organizations, such as the American Foundation for the Blind and the American Foundation for the Overseas Blind (which is now called Helen Keller Worldwide). Between 1946 and 1957, she went around the world speaking about the experiences and rights of people who are blind. Helen also inspired many works of art, including two Oscar-winning movies, and she received dozens of awards, such as the Presidential Medal of Freedom. That is the highest honor that an American civilian can receive.

Directions

Choose the item that best answers each question about the selection you just read. Circle the letter next to the answer.

13 The author's attitude toward Helen Keller is best described as

(A) admiring.

B critical.

C neutral.

D affectionate.

14 What caused Helen to understand the meaning of the word *water*?

F Anne tapped the ground and then spelled the word into Helen's hand.

G Anne spelled the word into Helen's hand while giving her a bath.

(H) Anne held Helen's hand under a pump and spelled the word into her hand.

J Anne spelled the word into Helen's hand while Helen drank some water.

15 Why did Helen work to gain respect for blind and deaf people?

A Helen loved and respected her teacher, Anne Sullivan.

(B) Helen knew how difficult it was to be unable to see and hear.

C Helen was able to speak even though she could not see or hear.

D Helen was from a small town called Tuscumbia, Alabama.

16 What effect did learning the meaning of W-A-T-E-R have on Helen?

F She grew more and more frustrated with Anne Sullivan.

(G) She immediately wanted to learn more words.

H She began writing a book about her life.

J She applied to Radcliffe College.

17 Which of the following did Helen do before she learned how to speak?

A She wrote her first book.

B She entered Radcliffe College.

(C) She learned the word for *Earth.*

D She gave many speeches.

18 Why was Helen Keller unable to see or hear?

F She was born unable to see or hear.

(G) She became very ill in her early childhood.

H She did not want to learn to read or write.

J She did not have a good teacher until she was seven.

19 What is special about the Presidential Medal of Freedom?

A The medal is worth a lot of money.

(B) The medal is the highest honor an American civilian can receive.

C The medal is only given to people who are blind.

D The medal is only given to people who have died.

20 What effect did Helen's life and achievements have on people who met or read about her?

F They felt sorry for her because she could not see or hear.

(G) They learned to respect people who were blind and deaf.

H They learned to "speak" to deaf people with their hands.

J They became close personal friends with Helen Keller.

GO ON

Common Core State Standards

Question 13: CCSS Informational Text 8. Explain how an author uses reasons and evidence to support particular points in a text, identifying which reasons and evidence support which point(s). **Questions 14–16, 18, 20: CCSS Informational Text 3.** Explain the relationships or interactions between two or more individuals, events, ideas, or concepts in a historical, scientific, or technical text based on specific information in the text. **Question 17: CCSS Informational Text 1.** Quote accurately from a text when explaining what the text says explicitly and when drawing inferences from the text. **Question 19: CCSS Informational Text 2.** Determine two or more main ideas of a text and explain how they are supported by key details; summarize the text.

WRITTEN RESPONSE TO THE SELECTION

Look Back and Write Look back at the battle scene on pages 267–271. The two monsters seem to be made of different parts. Explain why the men on the raft think they are seeing "half a dozen monsters, or more." Provide evidence to support your answer.

The information in the box below will help you remember what you should think about when you write your composition.

REMEMBER—YOU SHOULD

☐ explain why the men on the raft think they are seeing "half a dozen monsters, or more."

☐ use details from both the illustrations and the text in your writing.

☐ make sure you include lists in your answer.

☐ use colorful and descriptive words in your writing to engage the reader.

☐ check your work for correct spelling, capitalization, punctuation, grammar, and sentences.

GO ON

┌─ **Common Core State Standards**

CCSS Writing 1.b. Provide logically ordered reasons that are supported by facts and details. (Also **CCSS Writing 1.d., CCSS Language 1.**)

VOCABULARY

Directions
Find the word or words with the same meaning as the underlined word. Circle the letter next to the answer.

1 To celebrate their <u>independence</u>, some countries have holidays.

A   leaders' birthdays

B   harvests

C   freedom from control

D   religious beliefs

2 He <u>scrawled</u> a note.

F   wrote carelessly

G   composed

H   opened quickly

J   received

3 His <u>economic</u> theory was not useful.

A   unique and untested

B   relating to income, goods, and services

C   complicated

D   relating to science and technology

4 Her art project had <u>overrun</u> the kitchen table.

F   decorated

G   destroyed

H   spread over

J   abandoned

5 The hotel has no <u>vacant</u> rooms.

A   average

B   cheap

C   extraordinary

D   unoccupied

GO ON

Common Core State Standards

Questions 1–5: CCSS Language 5.c. Use the relationship between particular words (e.g., synonyms, antonyms, homographs) to better understand each of the words.

WORD ANALYSIS

Directions

Find the word or words with the same meaning as the underlined word. Circle the letter next to the answer.

6 Grandma's <u>retirement</u> starts next Monday.

   F hospitalization

   G long voyage overseas

   H agreement to do volunteer work

   (J) state of being finished with regular paying jobs

7 Matthew climbed the cliff <u>unaided</u>.

   A helped by someone

   B ignored by others

   (C) not helped by anyone

   D out of breath

8 Mom's car is <u>undriveable</u>.

   F fixed and ready to drive

   G nearly out of gas

   H brand new

   (J) not capable of being driven

9 He <u>disliked</u> that scary movie.

   A enjoyed

   (B) didn't like

   C approved of

   D told others about

10 Words could not express her <u>happiness</u>.

   F peaceful feeling

   G state of not depending on anyone else

   H misery

   (J) feeling of gladness

11 This disc is <u>rewriteable</u>.

   (A) able to be written on again and again

   B able to be played again and again

   C unable to be written on

   D damaged and unusable

12 It was a <u>joyless</u> trip for all of us.

   F happy

   G indifferent

   H forgettable

   (J) unhappy

GO ON

> **Common Core State Standards**

Questions 6–12: CCSS Language 5.c. Use the relationship between particular words (e.g., synonyms, antonyms, homographs) to better understand each of the words.

Name _____

COMPREHENSION

Chocolate from Trees

Did you know that three out of four Americans like chocolate? In some countries in Europe, nine out of ten people are chocolate lovers. Chocolate doesn't start out wrapped in paper or foil. It grows on trees!

The heavenly taste of chocolate comes from a plant called the cacao (kuh KOW) tree. Natives of the New World were the first to taste cacao's chocolate flavor hundreds of years ago. Europeans learned this tasty secret when they first came to America. Now chocolate belongs to the world.

The cacao tree grows well in places that are warm and rainy all year. Tiny, waxy, pink or white flowers sprout from the tree branches or trunk. These later turn into green or red seed pods. In time, the pods grow as long as twelve inches. Workers harvest the pods by hacking them off the tree. Then they use a hammer to break each pod open. Inside the pod's sticky pulp are twenty to fifty seeds called cocoa beans. The beans have to be cleaned and dried before they are bagged and shipped afar—to make chocolate.

Some cacao farmers tend thousands of trees and produce shiploads of cocoa beans while others run small farms with help from family members. Some farmers even grow their trees in rain forests among other trees. The trees grow long, full pods just fine that way.

Cacao farmers must tend their trees carefully. Cacao trees produce useful numbers of pods only after they reach the age of four or five years. Diseases and insects can attack the trees and pods. Funguses such as witches' broom and frosty pod can badly harm the pods and the cocoa beans. A virus called swollen shoot can kill the tree. Insects, such as mealybugs and borers, can damage pods and leaves.

So enjoy your chocolate! Lots of care and hard work went into it.

Key: cacao-growing areas

Directions

Choose the item that best answers each question about the selection you just read. Circle the letter next to the answer.

13 Study the map. Which statement best describes where cacao trees grow?

   A in Africa

   B in northern lands

   C near the equator

   D on islands

14 Who first used chocolate as food?

   F the Chinese

   G Natives of the New World

   H Europeans

   J people living in Africa

15 Which generalization can you make after reading the first paragraph?

   A Chocolate is not popular in Europe.

   B Most people do not like chocolate.

   C Many people around the world like chocolate.

   D Nine-tenths of the world's people like chocolate.

16 Which generalization about the world's cacao farms is true?

   F There is a wide variety of cacao farms.

   G All cacao farms start on completely cleared land.

   H All cacao farms are family affairs.

   J All cacao farms are huge plantations.

17 Which generalization can you make about paragraphs 3, 4, and 5?

   A Cacao trees grow in all climates.

   B Funguses and insects are good for cacao trees.

   C Cacao trees are easy to take care of.

   D Cacao farming is hard work.

18 Which is *not* a threat to the cacao tree?

   F seed pods

   G witches' broom

   H swollen shoot

   J mealybugs

19 Which generalization about farming cacao is true?

   A You have to deal with a variety of harmful diseases and insects.

   B You have to grow the trees for ten years before you have a crop.

   C You have to wrap the dried cocoa beans in paper or foil.

   D You have to grow the trees in bright sunlight.

20 The journey from cacao bean to the chocolate you eat

   F is quick and easy.

   G is a ten-year journey.

   H needs contributions from many people.

   J is by way of Europe.

GO ON

Common Core State Standards

Question 13: CCSS Informational Text 7. Draw on information from multiple print or digital sources, demonstrating the ability to locate an answer to a question quickly or to solve a problem efficiently. **Questions 14, 18: CCSS Informational Text 2.** Determine two or more main ideas of a text and explain how they are supported by key details; summarize the text. **Questions 15–17, 19–20: CCSS Informational Text 1.** Quote accurately from a text when explaining what the text says explicitly and when drawing inferences from the text.

WRITTEN RESPONSE TO THE SELECTION

> **Look Back and Write** Reread pages 297–298. What business buildings would you find on the streets of a town when it was thriving, before it became a ghost town? Sketch and label a typical ghost town's business area. Provide evidence to support your answer.

The information in the box below will help you remember what you should think about when you write your composition.

REMEMBER—YOU SHOULD

☐ explain what business buildings you would find on the streets of a town when it was thriving, and sketch and label a typical ghost town's business area.

☐ make sure you choose relevant details from both the text and the illustrations.

☐ use your imagination and prior knowledge as well as details from the text to answer the question.

☐ label your sketch clearly so that it is easy for the reader to follow.

☐ check your work for correct spelling, capitalization, punctuation, grammar, and sentences.

Common Core State Standards

CCSS Writing 2.b. Develop the topic with facts, definitions, concrete details, quotations, or other information and examples related to the topic. (Also **CCSS Writing 4.**, **CCSS Language 1.**)

VOCABULARY

Directions

Find the word or words with the same meaning as the underlined word. Circle the letter next to the answer.

1 Let me tell you about the <u>bizarre</u> adventure I had.

(A) strange
B dangerous
C exciting
D dull

2 The shepherd gave a <u>high-pitched</u> call.

F musical and pretty
G bright and clear
H low and loud
(J) shrill and piercing

3 It is <u>vital</u> that you pay attention.

A interesting, fascinating
(B) important, crucial
C scarce, rare
D prompt, on time

4 The president's speech was <u>breathtaking</u>.

F forceful
G hard to understand
H long
(J) astonishing

5 The pigeons came to <u>roost</u> on the roof.

(A) perch
B eat
C sleep
D fly

6 DEWEY DEFEATS TRUMAN is a famous <u>headline</u> in history.

F title of a work of fiction
G title of a play
(H) title of a newspaper article
J title of a poem

GO ON

Common Core State Standards

Questions 1–6: CCSS Language 5.c. Use the relationship between particular words (e.g., synonyms, antonyms, homographs) to better understand each of the words.

WORD ANALYSIS

Directions

Find the compound word in each sentence. Circle the letter next to the answer.

7 Monica shouldn't have used so much hairspray and blush.

- A shouldn't
- B used
- Ⓒ hairspray
- D blush

8 The detective leaned back in the armchair and closed his eyes in thought.

- F detective
- Ⓖ armchair
- H eyes
- J thought

9 My sister woke up too late to eat breakfast.

- A sister
- B woke up
- C late
- Ⓓ breakfast

10 Our house is not as tall as the evergreen tree in the yard.

- F house
- G tall
- Ⓗ evergreen
- J yard

11 The servant climbed a ladder to clean the chandelier in the big ballroom.

- A servant
- B ladder
- C chandelier
- Ⓓ ballroom

12 You can wear an overcoat, a jacket, a warm sweater, or a poncho.

- Ⓕ overcoat
- G jacket
- H sweater
- J poncho

COMPREHENSION

Tiger, Tiger

Tigers can be found in China, India, Nepal, and Siberia. People who study wild cats believe the first tigers came from Siberia and North China. These are very cold parts of the world. Even today, tigers prefer to spend hot afternoons in shady places. All other cats are famous for hating water, but tigers are different. They are good swimmers and enjoy a dip on a very hot day.

While lions live on the dusty plains, tigers prefer forests and jungles. Their striped coats help them blend in with their forest surroundings. Like all cats, they are quiet and stealthy in

GO ON

Common Core State Standards

Questions 7–12: CCSS Foundational Skills 3.a. Use combined knowledge of all letter-sound correspondences, syllabication patterns, and morphology (e.g., roots and affixes) to read accurately unfamiliar multisyllabic words in context and out of context.

motion. A tiger's prey is rarely aware of its presence until the tiger leaps upon it from the bushes. However, the wolves and lynxes that tigers eat can run fast, and tigers fail to catch their prey more often than they succeed. They also hunt young elephants, wild pigs, and buffalo.

Most tigers have orange fur with bold black stripes. Their eyes are yellow. Once in a while, a tiger is born with white fur. These special, rare tigers have brown stripes and blue eyes. Except for their coloring, they look just like all other tigers.

A tigress usually has two or three cubs at once. Sometimes she has as many as seven. She finds a den to live in with her cubs until they are big enough to take care of themselves. This takes about eighteen months. During that time, the tigress hunts for food. She drags her kill back to the den to feed her cubs.

Most tigers weigh from 250 to 500 pounds. The largest tigers weigh much more, sometimes as much as 700 pounds. This makes tigers the largest of cat species except for lions.

Some Americans break the law by trying to keep tigers as pets. It sounds like fun to cuddle a tiger cub and feed it milk from a bottle, but the tiger will soon grow to its full size. Imagine trying to keep a pet that may be four times as big as you are!

It's expensive to feed a tiger all the raw meat it needs (up to 60 pounds of meat in one meal!). Besides, tigers like to roam. In the wild, a tiger may travel thirty miles in a day. It's not possible for a pet tiger to have any freedom, because such a big, strong animal poses a danger to people. So a pet tiger must live in a small, confined space. In most states, it is against the law to have an exotic animal like a tiger as a pet. This is to protect both the animal and the citizens.

Directions

Choose the item that best answers each question about the selection you just read. Circle the letter next to the answer.

13 You can conclude that tigers enjoy spending time in the water because

(A) swimming cools them off and makes them more comfortable.

B they are unlike other cats in every way including this.

C they have striped coats that make them hard to see.

D water is a way to escape predators that can't swim.

14 What can you conclude from the information in paragraph 7?

F Cats are very popular pets in the United States.

(G) People should not try to keep tigers as pets.

H Tigers have fierce tempers that make them dangerous.

J Tigers like to roam in the wild.

15 Since a tiger can eat up to 60 pounds of meat at once, you can conclude that

A most tigers are choosy about what they eat.

B most tigers are overweight.

C it must drink a lot of water.

(D) it usually preys on large animals.

16 Which statement is a generalization?

F A tigress drags her kill back to the den to feed her cubs.

G White tigers have brown stripes and blue eyes.

H Tigers come from China, India, Nepal, and Siberia.

(J) Most tigers are orange with black stripes and yellow eyes.

17 Why did the author write this article?

A to tell people where they can learn more about tigers

B to entertain readers with exciting true stories about tigers

(C) to inform readers of some interesting facts about tigers

D to persuade readers that tigers make great pets

18 You might conclude that one reason small zoos may not have tigers is that

(F) it is expensive to care for and feed a tiger.

G people are scared of tigers.

H tigers are boring to watch.

J the larger zoos have taken all the tigers.

19 From the information in paragraph 7, you can reasonably conclude that a tiger kept as a pet would be

A friendly.

B big.

(C) unhappy.

D hungry.

20 In which way are tigers most like lions?

F They love the water.

(G) They move very quietly.

H They prefer cooler weather.

J They have striped coats.

GO ON

┌─ **Common Core State Standards** ─

Questions 13–15, 17–20: CCSS Informational Text 3. Explain the relationships or interactions between two or more individuals, events, ideas, or concepts in a historical, scientific, or technical text based on specific information in the text. **Question 16: CCSS Informational Text 1.** Quote accurately from a text when explaining what the text says explicitly and when drawing inferences from the text.

WRITTEN RESPONSE TO THE SELECTION

Look Back and Write Reread the saying on page 331: "The more you know about bugs, the less they bug you." What does the saying mean? Do you agree with this saying when it's applied to bats? Provide evidence from the article to support your answer.

The information in the box below will help you remember what you should think about when you write your composition.

REMEMBER—YOU SHOULD

☐ explain what the saying on page 331 means and whether you agree or disagree when it is applied to bats.

☐ make sure to explain the two meanings of the word *bug* in the first part of your answer.

☐ state your opinion clearly and provide reasons to support your opinion.

☐ check your work for correct spelling, capitalization, punctuation, grammar, and sentences.

GO ON

Common Core State Standards

CCSS Literature 4. Determine the meaning of words and phrases as they are used in a text, including figurative language such as metaphors and similes. (Also **CCSS Writing 1.a., CCSS Writing 1.b., CCSS Writing 1.c., CCSS Language 1., CCSS Language 3.**)

VOCABULARY

Directions

Find the word or words with the same meaning as the underlined word. Circle the letter next to the answer.

1 He **bleached** his hair.

  A dyed

  B curled

  C straightened

  Ⓓ whitened

2 Vultures flew above the **carcasses**.

  F craters

  Ⓖ bodies of dead animals

  H coast

  J skeletons of tiny insects

3 His **suspicions** were correct.

  A methods

  Ⓑ feelings

  C conclusions

  D ideas accepted without question

4 They died because of **starvation**.

  Ⓕ hunger

  G old age

  H illness

  J accident

5 The puppy was **scrawny**.

  A awkward

  B uneasy

  Ⓒ bony

  D timid

6 The buildings were in a state of **decay**.

  Ⓕ wearing away

  G being restored

  H tilting sideways

  J being purchased

7 She hiked across the **tundra**.

  A snow-covered island

  B vast, frozen lake

  C ice-covered valley

  Ⓓ cold, flat, treeless land

GO ON

⎧ **Common Core State Standards** ⎫

Questions 1–7: CCSS Language 5.c. Use the relationship between particular words (e.g., synonyms, antonyms, homographs) to better understand each of the words.

WORD ANALYSIS

Directions
Find the word or words with the same meaning as the underlined word. Circle the letter next to the answer.

8 The <u>steppes</u> of eastern Asia are very cold.

   F caves

   G mountains

   (H) plains

   J valleys

9 The <u>czar</u> did not like it when people disobeyed his orders.

   (A) emperor

   B owner

   C supervisor

   D customer

10 The mall's new parking lot is <u>mammoth</u>.

   F smooth

   (G) huge

   H covered

   J small

11 These <u>blintzes</u> are delicious.

   A crackers

   B small cakes

   C cookies

   (D) filled pancakes

12 The <u>samovar</u> was old but worked well.

   (F) large teapot

   G stove

   H freezer

   J furnace

GO ON

Common Core State Standards

Questions 8–12: CCSS Language 5.c. Use the relationship between particular words (e.g., synonyms, antonyms, homographs) to better understand each of the words.

COMPREHENSION

The Silk Road

The Silk Road was a major trade route between Asia and Europe. It was over five thousand miles long. A nineteenth-century geologist named it for silk, which comes from China.

Silk was one of the first items brought to the West from China. Cloth made from the cocoons of silkworms is very soft. In the Roman Empire, people traded an ounce of gold for an ounce of silk!

People, goods, and ideas moved along the Silk Road. Traders rode camels across huge deserts and through narrow mountain passes. In addition to silk, goods including perfume, grapes, and beautiful gems came and went by way of the Silk Road. Ideas traveled too. Buddhism, for example, spread outward from India and became a major religion in China.

No one is sure how the Silk Road began. During the Qin dynasty (221 B.C.–206 B.C.), many invaders attacked China. The emperor built the Great Wall of China to protect his lands. He didn't allow trade outside his country.

During the Han dynasty (202 B.C.–A.D. 220), a different emperor sent a group to meet with a strong state to the west named Persia. He wanted to know more about the world outside his country. The group did not return for twelve years. Its leader reported that Persia was too far away. However, he thought China could trade with that state.

Around 110 B.C., trade began between China and Persia. But bandits in the desert and mountains kept robbing traders along the route. Han leaders realized that they couldn't control the whole route alone. They needed local villages to make the route safe for the traders. Once these were set up, trade grew. Many villages became bigger cities and towns. Some of their customs traveled back to China.

By the second century B.C., trade also began between China and the Roman Empire. Silk passed from one group of traders to another until it arrived in Rome. It took two years, making the trip too far for one person. The power of the Han Chinese and the Romans grew. Neither group knew much about the other. The Romans called the Han Chinese the "silk people." They thought silk grew on trees!

After many centuries sea routes replaced the Silk Road. The long exchange of ideas had a big impact in China. It also started a connection between China and the West that is still strong today.

GO ON

Directions

Choose the item that best answers each question about the selection you just read. Circle the letter next to the answer.

13 In this nonfiction passage, the author mainly

A shows the effects of traveling the Silk Road on traders.

B encourages readers to visit the Silk Road.

C tells about the history of the Silk Road.

D describes the sights and sounds of the Silk Road.

14 People in the Roman Empire considered silk

F very rough.

G easy to make.

H very valuable.

J too expensive.

15 Goods were transported along the Silk Road by

A camels.

B carriages.

C bandits.

D silkworms.

16 Information in the passage supports the idea that

F there were no religions in China until Buddhism.

G Chinese emperors were kind to their subjects.

H silk was discovered by the Romans.

J ancient China was a very large and isolated country.

17 Based on the passage, when did villages begin appearing along the Silk Road?

A when bandits began robbing the traders

B when silk became popular

C when China needed places to meet with Roman traders

D when big Chinese cities became too crowded

18 What information supports the idea that China and Persia were very far from each other?

F Buddhism became a major religion in China.

G The group sent to Persia by the Han emperor did not return for twelve years.

H Bandits attacked travelers on the Silk Road.

J Villages were formed along the Silk Road.

19 Approximately how much time elapses in this passage?

A 15 years

B 200 years

C less than 100 years

D more than 1,000 years

20 What is the main idea of this passage?

F Traveling on the Silk Road was long and difficult.

G The Silk Road was an important link between China and the West.

H The Silk Road was one of many trade routes in China.

J Without silk, China would be isolated and unsuccessful.

GO ON

Common Core State Standards

Questions 13–14, 19: CCSS Informational Text 1. Quote accurately from a text when explaining what the text says explicitly and when drawing inferences from the text. **Questions 15–18, 20: CCSS Informational Text 2.** Determine two or more main ideas of a text and explain how they are supported by key details; summarize the text.

WRITTEN RESPONSE TO THE SELECTION

Look Back and Write Read the end of the selection on page 359. The author's last line in the selection talks about disaster striking. Why did disaster strike for the reindeer? Write an explanation to this question. Provide evidence to support your answer.

The information in the box below will help you remember what you should think about when you write your composition.

REMEMBER—YOU SHOULD

☐ explain why disaster struck the reindeer on Saint Matthew Island.

☐ put the events in sequence and use time-order words to indicate the sequence.

☐ organize your ideas clearly as you write so that the reader understands what you are saying.

☐ use details and facts from the text as evidence to support your answer.

☐ check your work for correct spelling, capitalization, punctuation, grammar, and sentences.

GO ON

Common Core State Standards

CCSS Writing 2. Write informative/explanatory texts to examine a topic and convey ideas and information clearly. (Also **CCSS Language 1., CCSS Language 3.**)

_____

_____

_____

_____

_____

_____

_____

_____

_____

_____

_____

_____

_____

_____

_____

_____

Name _____

VOCABULARY

Directions

Find the word or words with the same meaning as the underlined word. Circle the letter next to the answer.

1 The statue of the bear was <u>lifeless</u>.

   A unbelievable

   B unseen

   C not valuable

   (D) not alive

2 She held a <u>spoonful</u> of cereal.

   F single serving size

   (G) as much as a spoon can hold

   H bowl filled to the top

   J amount equal to a sugar cube

3 He works with <u>precious</u> metals.

   (A) valuable

   B scrap

   C common

   D unfamiliar

4 It was a peaceful <u>realm</u>.

   (F) area ruled by a king or queen

   G colony

   H land surrounded by water

   J community

5 She liked to <u>adorn</u> her hair with flowers.

   A scent

   (B) decorate

   C comb

   D refresh

6 I need to <u>cleanse</u> the wound.

   F inspect

   G bandage

   H stitch

   (J) wash

GO ON

> **Common Core State Standards**

Questions 1–6: CCSS Language 5.c. Use the relationship between particular words (e.g., synonyms, antonyms, homographs) to better understand each of the words.

WORD ANALYSIS

Directions

For each sentence, choose the item that shows the correctly spelled word. Circle the letter next to the word that fills the blank.

7 Today is a _____ day.
- A sphecial
- B speshial
- C special
- D spechial

8 The diamonds are very _____.
- F precious
- G prezhious
- H prechious
- J preschious

9 I am entering a piano _____.
- A competishun
- B competischun
- C competision
- D competition

10 We need to make a _____ decision.
- F cruxial
- G crucial
- H crushial
- J cruschial

11 The thunderstorm was _____.
- A ferocious
- B feroshious
- C ferochious
- D feroshous

12 Our host was _____.
- F grasious
- G grashious
- H gracious
- J graschious

COMPREHENSION

Saving Spring:
A Myth from Scandinavia

Once, in the northernmost regions of the world, winter came and never left. People had endured long winters before. But as the calendar turned to April and May, the snow kept falling, and the sun would not shine.

By June people in a local village grew fearful. They were unable to plant crops and afraid that they might starve. Snowdrifts towered so high that the villagers were isolated from other villages.

GO ON

Common Core State Standards

Questions 7–12: CCSS Language 2.e. Spell grade-appropriate words correctly, consulting references as needed.

The mayor called an emergency meeting in the town hall. A roaring fire did little to reduce the chill in the air. Villagers sat huddled together on the wooden benches, trying to keep warm. Outside another snowstorm raged, wind and snow swirling together.

The mayor said, "Spring is being held prisoner by Old Man Winter at the North Pole. Several villages and towns have sent their bravest people to rescue her, but none have returned. They want us to send someone now."

Everyone looked around, but no one volunteered. Then a young man named Oscar said, "I will go to the North Pole and see if I can rescue Spring. I don't mind the cold, and someone needs to challenge Old Man Winter."

A few weeks later, Oscar saw Old Man Winter's huge ice castle looming in the distance at the North Pole. It was as enormous as a mountain. He looked for a side entrance to try to sneak his way in, but before he knew what was happening, three guards captured him and dragged him into the icy palace. They put him in a large room that was empty except for a few rabbits and deer shivering from the cold. Surprised, Oscar collapsed onto a bench to rest and fell into a deep sleep.

When Oscar awoke, he discovered that his hands were now paws. He had turned into a huge tiger! A white rabbit sat a short distance away. Forgetting everything, Oscar only knew he was hungry. He chased the rabbit, but it was too fast. It led Oscar into a dark corridor.

After a while, Oscar sat down on the rough ground. His actions horrified him. Tears filled his eyes, and he hid his head between his paws. "It's all right, my friend," the rabbit's small voice said from a hole in the wall. "This is what Old Man Winter does to people when they come here to save Spring. He turns them into animals and they forget their humanity."

"Who are you?" Oscar asked.

"I am Greta," said the rabbit, coming out of the hole. "I am from a small village in the North. All of the villagers and our animals froze. As the only survivor, I try to help anyone who wants to save Spring. Little did we know what Old Man Winter had in mind. Many people roam the ice fields in animal form, having completely forgotten who they were. Saving Spring is our only chance of survival!"

GO ON

Directions

Choose the item that best answers each question about the selection you just read. Circle the letter next to the answer.

13 The winter described in the passage is different from other winters because

   A it doesn't snow.

   B the wind makes snowdrifts.

   (C) it doesn't end.

   D the skies are gray.

14 How is Oscar different from other people in his village?

   F He doesn't want to challenge Old Man Winter.

   (G) He doesn't mind the cold.

   H He is friendly with the mayor.

   J He has been to the North Pole.

15 In paragraph 6, Old Man Winter's ice castle is compared to

   A a monster.

   B a tiger.

   (C) a mountain.

   D a snowstorm.

16 What is the main problem that Oscar faces in the story?

   (F) trying to rescue Spring

   G trying to get to the North Pole

   H trying to speak to Old Man Winter

   J trying to turn Greta into a rabbit

17 At the end of the passage, what can you conclude will happen next?

   A Oscar will eat Greta.

   B Old Man Winter will let Spring go.

   C Oscar will bring Greta back to his village.

   (D) Greta and Oscar will work together to save Spring.

18 As someone holding Spring captive, Old Man Winter could best be compared to

   F a knight on a quest in a foreign land.

   G a hunter seeking big game.

   H a prince seeking a princess.

   (J) a king seeking power over others.

19 Both Oscar and Greta are

   A friends of Old Man Winter.

   (B) turned into animals by Old Man Winter.

   C enemies of Spring.

   D turned into animals by Spring.

20 After reading the passage, you can conclude that Oscar is

   F mean.

   (G) brave.

   H lonely.

   J hungry.

GO ON

Common Core State Standards

Questions 13–15, 18–19: CCSS Literature 3. Compare and contrast two or more characters, settings, or events in a story or drama, drawing on specific details in the text (e.g., how characters interact). **Question 16: CCSS Literature 2.** Determine a theme of a story, drama, or poem from details in the text, including how characters in a story or drama respond to challenges or how the speaker in a poem reflects upon a topic; summarize the text. **Questions 17, 20: CCSS Literature 1.** Quote accurately from a text when explaining what the text says explicitly and when drawing inferences from the text.

WRITTEN RESPONSE TO THE SELECTION

> **Look Back and Write** The "Midas touch" is a saying some people use. Reread pages 384–387. What do you think the "Midas touch" means? Write a possible definition of the saying. Provide evidence to support your answer.

The information in the box below will help you remember what you should think about when you write your composition.

REMEMBER—YOU SHOULD

☐ explain what you think the "Midas touch" means.

☐ draw conclusions about King Midas based on details in the story.

☐ write your definition clearly in a sentence that the reader can easily understand.

☐ make sure you include details from the story to support your definition.

☐ check your work for correct spelling, capitalization, punctuation, grammar, and sentences.

GO ON

> **Common Core State Standards**

CCSS Language 5.b. Recognize and explain the meaning of common idioms, adages, and proverbs. (Also **CCSS Literature 4.**, **CCSS Writing 1.a.**, **CCSS Writing 1.b.**, **CCSS Writing 1.c.**, **CCSS Language 1.**, **CCSS Language 3.**, **CCSS Language 5.b.**)

VOCABULARY

Directions
Find the word or words with the same meaning as the underlined word. Circle the letter next to the answer.

1 The heavy rain was <u>drenching</u> the hikers.
- (A) soaking
- B flushing
- C trampling
- D examining

2 They worked for peace during the <u>era</u> of fighting.
- F season
- G height
- H confusion
- (J) period of time

3 The artist is <u>criticizing</u> his students' work.
- A showing approval of
- B displaying
- (C) finding faults with
- D classifying

4 There was an <u>explosion</u> in the town.
- F astonishing sight
- (G) violent burst
- H accidental discovery
- J fortunate event

5 The boat <u>cruised</u> on the river.
- A appeared
- (B) traveled
- C stalled
- D wrecked

6 The students explored the uses of <u>hydrogen</u>.
- (F) a light gas
- G a chemical cleaner
- H a liquid cement
- J a frozen substance

GO ON

Common Core State Standards

Questions 1–6: CCSS Language 5.c. Use the relationship between particular words (e.g., synonyms, antonyms, homographs) to better understand each of the words.

WORD ANALYSIS

Directions
Find the word or words with the closest meaning to the underlined word. Circle the letter next to the answer.

7 The <u>critic</u> did not like the movie.

    A doctor

    (B) reviewer

    C lawyer

    D professor

8 He considered her <u>criticism</u> unnecessary.

    (F) unfavorable remarks

    G silly jokes

    H inappropriate comments

    J kind compliments

9 Talks between workers and management are at a <u>critical</u> stage.

    A unimportant

    B surprising

    C angry

    (D) important

10 I did not mean to <u>criticize</u> you.

    F laugh at

    G argue with

    (H) find fault with

    J turn away from

11 The <u>criteria</u> for making decisions are complex.

    A arrangements

    (B) standards

    C exceptions

    D schedules

12 He wrote a <u>critique</u> of the unfinished book.

    F chapter

    G essay

    (H) review

    J letter to the editor

GO ON

Common Core State Standards

Questions 7–12: CCSS Language 5.c. Use the relationship between particular words (e.g., synonyms, antonyms, homographs) to better understand each of the words.

Name _____

COMPREHENSION

Latin America:
Where North and South Meet

Latin America is the most beautiful and varied region in the world. It includes ancient ruins, modern cities, and quiet villages. There are rain forests, beaches, and mountains. Latin America has something to please the taste of any person.

Latin America includes Mexico, the Caribbean islands, the countries of Central America, and the continent of South America. Most Latin Americans speak Spanish or Portuguese. Many also speak English, French, and other languages.

Latin America has vast rain forests. Rain forests are large forests of tall trees. They grow in places that are warm all year and get lots of rain. Many endangered animals live in rain forests. It is important that people find a way to help save these animals from disappearing.

The longest mountain range on Earth is also found in Latin America. The Andes Mountains run over five thousand miles through seven countries. One of their peaks is the highest in the Western Hemisphere. The Andes is the most majestic of all mountain ranges in the world.

History in Latin America may go back as far as thirty thousand years. It was home to many civilizations long before Columbus and other European explorers arrived in the fifteenth century. One of the most important was the Mayan civilization.

The Maya built their first villages in Latin America around 1500 B.C. By A.D. 250 they had built many large cities. The Maya had a written language, practiced astronomy, and developed a 365-day calendar, among other accomplishments. The ruins of many Mayan cities remain. As many as six million Latin Americans still speak Mayan languages.

European customs changed Latin America a great deal. Explorers brought new weapons, new languages, and a new religion. This was Christianity. They also brought slaves from Africa to work in Latin America. Many native traditions and customs were lost.

Today, Latin America mixes European and native cultures. A good example is music. Latin American music has several different styles that blend Spanish, Native American, and African rhythms. Some of the most popular forms are samba, tango, and reggae.

GO ON

Directions

Choose the item that best answers each question about the selection you just read. Circle the letter next to the answer.

13 Latin America could best be described as a region of

   A little population.

   B small size.

   (C) many influences.

   D beautiful scenery.

14 Which of the following is a statement of opinion?

   (F) Latin America is the most beautiful and varied region in the world.

   G It includes ancient ruins, modern cities, and quiet villages.

   H Latin America has vast rain forests.

   J Rain forests are large forests of tall trees.

15 Which statement could not be proved by checking a reference source?

   A The longest mountain range on Earth is in Latin America.

   B The Andes Mountains run over five thousand miles.

   C One of their peaks is the highest in the Western hemisphere.

   (D) The Andes is the most majestic mountain range in the world.

16 Which would be the best reference source to check the article's statements about the Mayan civilization?

   F an atlas

   G a biography

   (H) a history book

   J a dictionary

17 Latin American history possibly dates back

   A 3,000 years.

   (B) 30,000 years.

   C 300,000 years.

   D 3 million years.

18 Which of the following contains a statement of opinion?

   (F) One of the most important was the Mayan civilization.

   G Latin America includes Mexico, the Caribbean islands, Central America, and South America.

   H The Maya built their first villages in Latin America around 1500 B.C.

   J The ruins of many Mayan cities remain.

19 This passage is mainly about

   (A) Latin American geography and history.

   B Latin American people and culture.

   C European explorers in Latin America.

   D European music in Latin America.

20 Which is a statement of fact?

   F It is important that people find a way to help save endangered animals.

   G The Andes is the most majestic of all mountain ranges.

   (H) The Maya had a written language and practiced astronomy.

   J Latin America has something to please the taste of any person.

GO ON

Common Core State Standards

Questions 13, 19: CCSS Informational Text 2. Determine two or more main ideas of a text and explain how they are supported by key details; summarize the text. **Questions 14–18, 20: CCSS Informational Text 1.** Quote accurately from a text when explaining what the text says explicitly and when drawing inferences from the text.

WRITTEN RESPONSE TO THE SELECTION

> **Look Back and Write** Reread the last sentence on page 421. Is it a statement of fact or an opinion? Do you agree or disagree with this statement? Write your answer. Provide evidence to support your answer.

The information in the box below will help you remember what you should think about when you write your composition.

REMEMBER—YOU SHOULD

☐ explain if the last sentence of the selection is a statement of fact or an opinion and if you agree or disagree with the statement.

☐ remember to explain to the reader why the sentence is a statement of fact or a statement of opinion.

☐ use prior knowledge and details from the text as evidence to support your answer to the second question.

☐ write persuasively to convince the reader of your argument.

☐ check your work for correct spelling, capitalization, punctuation, grammar, and sentences.

GO ON

⟩ **Common Core State Standards**

CCSS Writing 1. Write opinion pieces on topics or texts, supporting a point of view with reasons and information. (Also **CCSS Writing 1.a., CCSS Writing 1.c., CCSS Writing 4., CCSS Language 1., CCSS Language 3.**)

VOCABULARY

Directions
Find the word or words with the same meaning as the underlined word. Circle the letter next to the answer.

1 My sister plays the <u>bass</u>.

   A type of horn

   (B) low-sounding stringed instrument

   C pair of small connected drums

   D an instrument played by pressing keys

2 The musicians <u>jammed</u>.

   F sang without instruments

   G made arrangements to play

   (H) played music without practicing

   J agreed to form a band

3 My uncle is <u>forgetful</u>.

   (A) likely not to remember

   B not sure of himself

   C interested in new things

   D likely to help those in need

4 He is saving his money for a <u>clarinet</u>.

   F microscope

   G painting of himself

   H microphone

   (J) woodwind instrument

5 Her little brother is <u>fidgety</u>.

   A dignified

   B quick to express anger

   C jealous

   (D) constantly moving

6 He buys <u>secondhand</u> books.

   (F) not new

   G not valuable

   H entertaining

   J tattered

7 Some birds sing at <u>nighttime</u>.

   A from morning to noon

   B the usual time for eating

   (C) from dusk to dawn

   D the beginning of summer

GO ON

Common Core State Standards

Questions 1–7: CCSS Language 5.c. Use the relationship between particular words (e.g., synonyms, antonyms, homographs) to better understand each of the words.

WORD ANALYSIS

Directions
Find the compound word in each sentence. Circle the letter next to the answer.

8 The hotel gave us an upgrade after we complained about our room's temperature.

F hotel

(G) upgrade

H complained

J temperature

9 My teacher told me to study several chapters in my textbook before the final exam.

A several

B chapters

(C) textbook

D exam

10 Some recent events at the bookstore include an author signing and a book discussion group.

F recent

(G) bookstore

H author

J discussion

11 As he constructed the armoire, he used sandpaper to smooth out all the knots in the lumber.

A constructed

B armoire

(C) sandpaper

D lumber

12 Detectives use many kinds of evidence to track down criminals, including fingerprints.

F detectives

G evidence

H criminals

(J) fingerprints

GO ON

Common Core State Standards

Questions 8–12: CCSS Foundational Skills 3.a. Use combined knowledge of all letter-sound correspondences, syllabication patterns, and morphology (e.g., roots and affixes) to read accurately unfamiliar multisyllabic words in context and out of context.

Name _____

COMPREHENSION

The Ant Army Attacks

General Lopez could see the soldiers approaching from his window, neatly arranged in phalanxes. The platoons were marching straight toward him, never deviating from their regimented route. It was not the first time they had approached. He was gravely concerned that it would not be the last time the problem would arise.

The general picked up the phone in his office and cleared his throat. "Get me Dr. Hamilton," he ordered wearily. "I need to speak to him about the insect invasion."

Thousands of ants had overtaken the general's base during the last few weeks. No one knew the cause or what the ants were looking for. Dr. Hamilton, a respected insect specialist, and several other scientists were working feverishly to alleviate the problem.

Dr. Hamilton responded quickly. "The ants are getting worse," the general told him. "You know how I feel about insects!" The general was afraid of insects, especially ants. Ants were an enemy he didn't know how to fight.

"I don't know what to tell you," Dr. Hamilton replied. "We tried giving them food, but they ignored it. We also tried spraying insecticide, but they kept coming back. These ants are definitely looking for something. But I don't know what."

General Lopez frowned. He looked down and scratched his knee. An ant was crawling on his leg. He tried not to panic. As soon as he moved his hand, the ant began scurrying away.

"General, are you still there?" Dr. Hamilton asked. "My colleague, Dr. Barker, just came into the lab. She has some new information. Let me put her on the phone."

"I just received some test results, General," Dr. Barker said excitedly. "The ants are severely dehydrated. They're seeking water, not food. There's been a drought in the local area recently. The top levels of the soil where they nest must have dried out. Without water, they die quickly. But there are billions of ants in the world. These scouts are desperately trying to find water."

Dr. Barker suggested turning on the base's sprinkler system. Because of the drought, it was not being used. The general agreed with the idea. Within seconds, sprinklers came on all over the base.

The general watched the ants change direction and head for the sprinklers. *Maybe ants aren't so bad after all,* he thought. *Ants are a little like people. Food is important, but they also need water to survive.*

GO ON

Directions

irections
Choose the item that best answers each question about the selection you just read. Circle the letter next to the answer.

13 Which event happens first?

   A General Lopez speaks to Dr. Barker about the ants.

   (B) The ants march toward the military base.

   C The general gives an order for the sprinklers to be turned on.

   D Dr. Hamilton confesses that he doesn't know what the ants want.

14 During his conversation with Dr. Hamilton, General Lopez

   F realizes that he is afraid of ants.

   G asks to speak to Dr. Barker.

   (H) sees an ant crawling on his leg.

   J suggests turning on the sprinkler system.

15 The ants in the story are

   A hot.

   (B) thirsty.

   C cold.

   D hungry.

16 Based on information in the story, the ants behave the way they do because of

   F a heat wave.

   (G) a drought.

   H a deep freeze.

   J a military battle.

17 At the end of the story, General Lopez learns

   A not to fight enemies.

   B how important scientists are.

   (C) not to fear ants.

   D how to stop a drought.

18 Which event happens last?

   (F) Dr. Barker explains why the ants have come to the base.

   G General Lopez realizes he's afraid of insects.

   H Dr. Hamilton suggests that the general speak to Dr. Barker.

   J General Lopez calls Dr. Hamilton.

19 After the sprinklers are turned on and the ants head for them, General Lopez

   A closes up his office for the rest of the day.

   B thanks Dr. Barker for her good advice.

   C puts an end to the drought in the area.

   (D) realizes that ants aren't so scary after all.

20 What do the ants in the story do after they get thirsty?

   (F) search for water

   G search for food

   H hide underground

   J die in large numbers

GO ON

Common Core State Standards

Questions 13–20: CCSS Literature 1. Quote accurately from a text when explaining what the text says explicitly and when drawing inferences from the text.

WRITTEN RESPONSE TO THE SELECTION

> **Look Back and Write** Reread the last two pages of the story. Where was Uncle Click's hat? Do you think it got there by accident? Provide evidence to support your answer.

The information in the box below will help you remember what you should think about when you write your composition.

REMEMBER—YOU SHOULD

☐ explain where Uncle Click's hat was and if you think it got there by accident.

☐ use the details in the last two pages of the story to draw a conclusion about how the hat got there.

☐ use details from the story to support your answer.

☐ make sure that each sentence you write helps the reader understand your composition.

☐ check your work for correct spelling, capitalization, punctuation, grammar, and sentences.

Common Core State Standards

CCSS Writing 1. Write opinion pieces on topics or texts, supporting a point of view with reasons and information. (Also **CCSS Literature 1., CCSS Language 1., CCSS Language 3.**)